Enid B

SUMMERTIME STORIES

Look out for all of these enchanting story collections
by *Enid Blyton*

Enid Blyton

SUMMERTIME STORIES

Hodder
Children's
Books

HODDER CHILDREN'S BOOKS

This collection first published in Great Britain in 2018
by Hodder & Stoughton

1 3 5 7 9 10 8 6 4 2

Enid Blyton ® and Enid Blyton's signature are Registered Trademarks
of Hodder & Stoughton Limited
Text © Hodder & Stoughton Limited, 2018
Illustrations © Hodder & Stoughton Limited, 2018

A CIP catalogue record for this book is available from the British Library.

ISBN 978 1 444 94259 0

Printed and bound in Great Britain by Clays Ltd, St Ives plc

The paper and board used in this book are made from wood from
responsible forests.

Hodder Children's Books
An imprint of Hachette Children's Group
Part of Hodder and Stoughton
Carmelite House
50 Victoria Embankment
London EC4Y 0DZ

An Hachette UK Company
www.hachette.co.uk
www.hachettechildrens.co.uk

Contents

Too Good to Be True!

Too Good to Be True!

BINKIE AND Tigger were cross. Their Aunt Work-a-Lot had just turned them out of her house without even a slice of bread and butter for their dinner!

'Mean old thing! Just because we didn't dig up her garden for her!' said Binkie.

'And she said we hadn't swept the backyard,' grumbled Tigger. 'What's the matter with the backyard? Why can't it be dirty? All this fuss about being clean and tidy and working hard for a living!'

They were walking beside the river. It flowed calmly along in the sunshine and looked very peaceful.

'It's a pity we were born pixies,' said Binkie gloomily. 'Why couldn't we be a river? Just flowing along because it can't do anything else. No cross aunt to make it rush here and there and do silly jobs.'

'I'm hot,' said Tigger, and he flung himself down beside the water. 'Here's a nice, warm, cosy little cove, Binkie. Let's bask in the sun.'

'We're supposed to go and fetch potatoes from the farm,' said Binkie, but he sat down beside Tigger all the same. 'Ah-h-h-h! How nice to be somewhere that Aunt Work-a-Lot isn't.'

They took off their shoes and stockings and put their feet into the warm water. Then they lay back, tipped their pixie caps over their ears and talked lazily.

'What we want is some good luck,' said Binkie. 'Just a little bit of good luck – like finding a shilling – or some wonderful spell.'

'I could do with finding some dinner,' said Tigger dolefully. 'I had hardly any breakfast. I'm terribly hungry. We are very badly treated, Binkie. We deserve a great *big* piece of good luck, not a little bit.'

Now a good way up the river was Mr Hey-There, the goblin. He had rowed all the way up against the stream, panting and puffing. He knew of a nice place to fish. He had brought a very fine lunch with him, a rubber sheet to sit on, a big umbrella in case it rained and two fat books to read if the fish didn't bite.

Aha! Mr Hey-There meant to have a very nice day indeed – plenty to eat, plenty to drink, plenty of fish to catch (he hoped) and books to read if he didn't.

He came to the place he wanted. He flung the boat's rope over a tree stump and jumped out. He took with him his fishing rod, meaning to get it ready first of all.

Then he grunted crossly. Three cows were staring at him from just nearby.

He didn't like cows. He didn't like anything that came and breathed down his neck whilst he was fishing. It frightened the fish in the water, and it made him feel very uncomfortable. He was always afraid that the horse or cow breathing over him might begin to nibble his hair, thinking it was grass.

So what did Mr Hey-There do but address the cows very sternly and tell them to go away at once.

'Hey, there!' he shouted. 'Shoo, go away!'

The cows chewed hard as they stood staring at him and didn't budge an inch. So Mr Hey-There had to chase them. First he chased one cow away, and then another, and then the third. By the time he had chased the third away to the other end of the field, the first two had come back to his fishing rod and were staring at it as if they thought it might be good to eat.

So Mr Hey-There had to begin his chasing all over again. It took a lot of time and was most annoying. But the most annoying thing of all was still to come.

When at last he had got all the cows at the other end of the field, and was back where he had left the boat, there was no boat!

It had gone. It simply wasn't there – nor were his

lunch, his books, his umbrella or his rubber sheet to sit on. Only his fishing rod was waiting for him.

Mr Hey-There stamped so hard on the bank in his rage that all the fish in the water nearby rushed off as if sharks were after them.

'It's gone!' raged Mr Hey-There. 'Floated off down the river by itself. Now I've got to walk miles down the bank to find it! What a day! All because of those three cows that came to breathe down my neck.'

The boat had indeed gone off by itself. The rope hadn't been made fast to the tree stump and had simply slid into the water. So the river had taken the boat, and it was now floating back gently and peacefully all the way it had come.

In fact, it floated right down to the little cove where Binkie and Tigger were lying, with their feet dabbling in the warm water. The current took the boat into the cove, and it bobbed over to the lazy pixies. They didn't see it because they were lying on their backs in the sun.

They were still talking about good luck. 'Some people have it and some people don't,' Binkie was saying. 'It's not fair.'

'Aunt Work-a-Lot always says that good luck comes to people who work for it,' said Tigger gloomily. 'Oh, Binkie, wouldn't it be nice to have a great big bit of good luck – something like a wish that came true?'

'If I had a wish, I'd wish for a jolly big lunch right away this very minute,' said Binkie.

Just at that moment the boat bumped gently against his toes. He thought it was Tigger's feet bumping him. 'Don't,' he said.

'Don't what?' asked Tigger in surprise.

'Don't push my feet,' said Binkie.

'I'm not,' said Tigger, and just then the boat pushed quite hard against all their four feet in the water.

'Don't!' they both said at once. 'Leave my feet alone!'

Tigger sat up crossly. He suddenly saw the boat.

'I say, Binkie! Look here! It's a boat!'

Binkie sat up, too. 'A boat! Golly! There's no one in it. Oh, Tigger, do you think it's been sent to us?'

'Who would have sent it?' said Tigger. 'Don't be silly.'

'It might be a bit of good luck suddenly arrived!' said Binkie. 'Boats never come without people in them. This must be a magic boat, a good-luck boat! A boat full of good things for us! Oh, Tigger!'

Tigger pulled the boat into the cove. 'My goodness – look at this basket of food!'

'Oh!' said Binkie, overcome with joy. 'My wish has come true. Don't you remember how I wished for a jolly good lunch, Tigger? I'll share it with you.'

'You'll *share* it?' said Tigger indignantly. 'I should think you will! It isn't yours. It's *ours*. The boat came to both of us.'

'All right, all right,' said Binkie, and he took the big basket of food out of the boat. There were two ginger beer bottles beside it.

'Look at those!' Tigger said joyfully. 'Our favourite drink!'

'What else is there?' asked Binkie. 'A rubber sheet for us to sit on. How very thoughtful! I did think the grass was a bit damp, didn't you, Tigger? And look – two lovely, fat storybooks to read when we've finished our dinner!'

'And even an umbrella in case it rains,' said Tigger. 'It might quite easily rain. Oh, Binkie, it looks as if somebody has planned a really lovely day for us – plenty to eat and drink, a groundsheet to sit on, books to read and an umbrella in case it rains. This must be the big piece of good luck we've been talking about.'

They took everything out of the boat. They spread the groundsheet on the grass, poked the umbrella down a rabbit hole to keep it safe, put the books beside them and opened the dinner-basket.

'Chicken sandwiches! My favourite!' said Binkie in delight.

'Egg and tomato! My favourite!' said Tigger

joyfully. 'Plum cake! Currant buns! Chocolate biscuits! Oh, Binkie, if this is the lunch you wished us, I must say you know what to wish for!'

They ate every single thing in the basket. They drank the ginger beer out of the bottles. They were just going to settle down in the sunshine to read their books when two cows came down to the water.

'Go away, cows,' said Binkie. 'Go to another part of the river to drink. This is our bit. Oh, look, Tigger, that cow is eating the paper bags. Shoo, cow, shoo!'

The cows wouldn't shoo, so the two pixies got up to chase them away. They ran up the river bank, shouting and yelling. The cows lumbered slowly away.

A little way up the river bank Binkie and Tigger met an angry-looking goblin. It was Mr Hey-There, still looking for his boat. He called to Binkie and Tigger.

'Hey, there! I want to ask you something.'

Binkie and Tigger didn't like goblins. They turned

away and began to walk back to their cove. Mr Hey-There put his two heavy hands on their shoulders.

'Now then! You'll answer my questions if I want you to.'

'Certainly, sir,' said Binkie in a fright, not liking the feel of the goblin's knobbly fingers at all.

'I'm looking for a boat,' said Mr Hey-There.

'Oh,' said Tigger at once. 'We've got one we can hire out to you, goblin.'

'I'm not looking for one to hire,' said Mr Hey-There. 'I'm looking for my own boat. And for my dinner that was in it.'

'D-d-d-dinner?' stammered Binkie, feeling rather faint all of a sudden.

'Yes, dinner,' said Mr Hey-There crossly. 'Have you never heard of dinner before? My dinner was chicken sandwiches, egg and tomato sandwiches, plum cake, currant buns, chocolate biscuits . . .'

'Was – was it really?' said Tigger, stammering too.

'What's the matter with you two pixies?' said Mr Hey-There. 'Stammering and stuttering and looking so silly! Have you seen my boat?'

'Well – we don't know if it was *your* boat,' began Binkie, wishing he was a hundred miles away. 'If you'd take your knobbly hands off our shoulders, goblin, we could lead you to where we know there is a boat.'

'You'll lead me to it *with* my hands on your shoulders,' said Mr Hey-There, beginning to feel there was something queer about all this. 'Now – quick march!'

And quick march it had to be! Down to the cove went all three – and then Mr Hey-There stood and gazed at his empty dinner-basket, his books, his ginger beer bottles and his rubber sheet. He saw the handle of his umbrella sticking out of the rabbit hole. He saw his boat, still nosing into the little cove.

'You've eaten my dinner! How dare you! You little thieves! You greedy, dishonest robbers! Now, you get into that boat and row me all the way upstream to the police station. Go on – get in. Bring that umbrella. It will do to poke you with when you row too slowly!' roared Mr Hey-There.

And into that boat Binkie and Tigger had to climb, and row it slowly for a whole mile up the river to where the little stone police station stood. How they panted and puffed! Mr Hey-There wouldn't allow them even a minute's rest. If one or other of them stopped rowing he would poke them with the end of his umbrella.

'Thieves and robbers,' he kept saying. He wouldn't listen to a word that Binkie and Tigger said.

'We thought it was a wish come true when your boat came,' cried Binkie. 'We thought it was a piece of good luck. We did really.'

It was no good saying anything at all. Mr Hey-There wouldn't listen. The big policeman wouldn't listen. And when they got Aunt Work-a-Lot to come along, she wouldn't listen either.

'They are just a couple of lazy rascals,' she said.

'They want a good telling-off each, and some hard work to do. That would put them right.'

Well, they got the telling-off, and Mr Hey-There gave them some hard work, too. He said they must row him home and spend a whole week with him, digging up his garden. That would pay for the dinner they had eaten.

'I shall never make a wish again,' said poor Binkie at the end of that dreadful week.

'I shall never hope for good luck again,' said Tigger.

'But oh – wasn't it *lovely* when we sat up on the river bank and saw that boat full of good things?' sighed Binkie.

Then back they had to go to Aunt Work-a-Lot. They had had to work so very hard at Mr Hey-There's that their aunt's little jobs seemed quite easy to do. She was pleased with them.

'You've quite changed for the better!' she said. 'Well, if you do that, so will I! I'll make you pineapple jelly with cherries and whipped cream on top for supper!'

Oooooh! Binkie and Tigger beamed at one another. What a bit of good luck. Perhaps things weren't going to be so bad after all!

Brer Rabbit's Strange Flower

Brer Rabbit's Strange Flower

ONCE UPON a time Brer Rabbit took his garden spade and dug out a little round bed right in the middle of his garden. He edged the bed with shells and watered the ground thoroughly.

'What are you doing, Brer Rabbit?' asked Brer Fox, leaning over the fence.

'Oh, good morning, Brer Fox,' said Brer Rabbit, very busy indeed. 'I'm just getting this bed ready for the marvellous Minny-Pinny Flower.'

'The *what*?' said Brer Fox, in astonishment. 'I've never heard of it.'

'Ah, I don't wonder,' said Brer Rabbit. 'It's a most

strange flower, Brer Fox. It has purple petals, a red centre, yellow leaves with blue spots and a most exciting smell. But the strange thing about it is that only those people who are truthful and honest can see it or smell it! Dishonest people can't see or smell the Minny-Pinny Flower at all!'

'My!' said Brer Fox, grinning. 'Then what's the use of *you* growing it, Brer Rabbit? You won't be able to see it when you want to plant it! Ho! ho! ho!'

He went off and left Brer Rabbit scowling. Soon the news about the marvellous Minny-Pinny Flower had spread and every day people came to see if it was there. One day Brer Hare saw Brer Rabbit digging a hole in the middle of the bed, and he watched to see what he was going to plant. Brer Rabbit pretended to pick up something and was very busy seeming to plant it in the hole. Then he patted down the earth, took his watering can and watered it thoroughly, and looked up at Brer Hare.

'Hey-ho, Brer Hare!' he said, grinning. 'You're just

in time to see me plant the strange Minny-Pinny Flower. Isn't it funny? Come in and smell it.'

Now Brer Hare had heard that only truthful and honest people could see the Minny-Pinny Flower – and he couldn't see anything in the bed at all. He was filled with horror. If he said he could see nothing Brer Rabbit would at once say, 'Oho, Brer Hare, you're dishonest, then – only dishonest people can't see my marvellous flower!' And then Brer Hare would feel perfectly dreadful! Whatever was he to do?

'Do come in,' said Brer Rabbit, opening his gate. 'Can't you smell the Minny-Pinny Flower from there? It's a most exciting scent.'

Brer Hare went in. He thought he had better pretend to see the flower and admire it. It would never do if people knew he couldn't see it. They would say he was dishonest at once. So he went up to the bed and bent over as if he were smelling the flower.

'Marvellous!' said Brer Hare. 'Oh, what a fine flower! How strange it is! How beautiful!'

Just then Brer Terrapin poked his nose in at the gate and saw Brer Hare admiring the flower that he, Brer Terrapin, couldn't see at all! *My!* thought Brer Terrapin. *If Brer Hare can see it, it must be there! I'd better pretend I can see something!*

So in he waddled and was soon pretending to smell the marvellous Minny-Pinny Flower, too. Brer Rabbit leant on his spade and looked pleased. 'It's a strange flower, isn't it?' said Brer Rabbit. 'And the smell – ah, stranger still! Truly a wonderful plant! Now, my friends, I shall soon know who is honest and who is dishonest in our town, for, as you know, dishonest people can neither see nor smell this plant!'

Brer Hare and Brer Terrapin went home, and on their way they told everyone about the strange Minny-Pinny Flower, and how they had seen it and smelt it – though, of course, they had seen nothing at all! Soon all the folk were hurrying to Brer Rabbit's to see the strange plant, and Brer Rabbit grinned and waved his hands as they leant over the fence.

'Hey-ho, Brer Bear! Hey-ho, Brer Wolf! Hey-ho, Brer Turkey Buzzard! What do you think of my lovely Minny-Pinny Flower? Come in and smell it. If you want seeds from it, I can sell you a packet at twopence a time!'

Now, of course, Brer Bear, Brer Wolf and Brer Turkey Buzzard could see nothing at all in the bed, but not one of them liked to say so. It would never do to let the others know such a thing – it would be dreadful to be thought dishonest or untruthful!

'Wonderful!' said Brer Bear.

'Marvellous!' said Brer Wolf.

'Such a fine scent!' said Brer Turkey Buzzard.

'It's a useful plant to have in your garden,' said Brer Rabbit. 'It soon shows you who tells the truth or not. Would anyone like any seeds?'

'I'll take a packet,' said Brer Bear, and Brer Wolf and Brer Turkey Buzzard said the same, so Brer Rabbit gave them each small envelopes – but when the three opened them to look at the seeds they could see nothing at all! Dear, dear, how dreadful not to be able to see even the seeds! They felt most ashamed, and hid it by exclaiming that the seeds were marvellous too! Then off they went home, talking about the Minny-Pinny Flower and their wonderful seeds, but all of them secretly very much worried because they could see nothing at all.

The next day everyone came to look over the fence again, hoping that they would be able to see the flower that morning. Brer Frog hopped up too, and goggled his big eyes at the bed – but Brer Frog was an outspoken person who never pretended anything at all. So he opened his wide mouth and croaked, 'Well, where's this marvellous flower? I can't see anything at all! There's nothing there – and you know it, Brer Rabbit! It's just one of your tricks!'

Everyone stared at Brer Rabbit – but he didn't turn a hair. No, not he! He leant on his spade and spoke very sadly. 'Brer Frog,' he said, 'you're quite right. My Minny-Pinny Flower died in the night, and I've dug it up. So there is nothing in the bed at all. But it told me who was truthful and who wasn't!'

Then everyone grew very red, for they knew Brer Rabbit had tricked them. One by one they stole away – all except Brer Frog, and he croaked at the grinning rabbit, 'You're a fraud, Brer Rabbit! Nothing but a fraud!'

'I'm no worse than anyone else,' said Brer Rabbit, grinning. 'Am I now?' And Brer Frog had nothing to say to that!

The Knotty
Handkerchief

The Knotty
Handkerchief

ONCE UPON a time Too-Hot went to shell peas in his
garden. He took out a chair, a basket of peas and a
dish to put them in. He sat down in the sunshine and
began to shell the peas.

It was a hot summer's day. It really was very
hot. Too-Hot puffed and panted, and wished he
had brought out a hat to wear. He was too lazy
to go in and get one so he took out his big yellow
handkerchief and made it into a nice cap by tying
a knot in each of the four corners. Then he slipped it
on his head and wore it like that. It kept the blazing
sun off his head.

When he had finished shelling the peas he went indoors. He took off his handkerchief cap and put it into his pocket, quite forgetting to untie the knots. There it stayed till the next day.

When Too-Hot got up next morning he pulled his yellow handkerchief out of his pocket to put in a clean one – and then he discovered that it had a knot in each corner.

Now Too-Hot always tied a knot in his handkerchief when he wanted to remind himself to remember something. He used to tie a knot when he wanted to buy some more bacon for breakfast, and he always tied one when he wanted to remember to take his little dog for a walk. So when he saw that his handkerchief had four knots in, he was most puzzled. It must have been something very important that made him tie four knots in, he thought.

He had forgotten that he had used his handkerchief for a sun cap! He sat down and thought hard for five minutes.

'Now what made me tie so many knots?' he wondered. 'Oh, dear, I wish I could remember! Is it somebody's birthday today? Or is somebody coming to tea with me? Or am I supposed to go and visit somebody? Whatever can it be? My dreadful memory! Oh, I wish I knew why I had tied all those knots in my handkerchief!'

Well, of course, Too-Hot couldn't remember why he had put those knots there, and it worried him dreadfully. He decided to go to Think-a-Lot the wise man and see if he could tell him the reason. So he took his purse and went.

Think-a-Lot looked at the yellow handkerchief with all the knots in, and frowned. He put it into a saucepan of purple milk and boiled it for five minutes. Then he took out the handkerchief, which was now spotted with purple, and squeezed it dry. He opened it and looked closely at it. Across it was written one word.

'Here's the reason that you knotted your

handkerchief,' he said. 'It's written across it for you to read.'

Too-Hot looked closely at it. 'It says "sunshine"!' he said. 'Sunshine! Now whatever does that mean? Why should I have knotted my handkerchief to remember sunshine? Dear, dear, dear, it's a greater puzzle than ever!'

He paid the wise man a silver sixpence, and went away, frowning hard. Sunshine? What did it mean? Was he to put something out in the sun to dry? Was that what he had wanted to remind himself to do?

Too-Hot couldn't think of anything at all. So he decided to go up the Tall Hill to Breezy Cottage, where Know-It-All the brownie lived. Know-It-All was very clever, and had such a good memory that he could often remember what other people forgot.

So up the Tall Hill went Too-Hot, carrying his knotty yellow handkerchief. Know-It-All was sitting outside his door, knitting a scarf of field-mist, very fine and delicate. It was wonderful to watch him.

32

He greeted Too-Hot with a smile and asked him what he wanted.

'I want to know if you can tell me why I put four knots in this handkerchief,' said Too-Hot. 'I always tie knots in my handkerchief when I want to remember anything important, but this time I can't remember why I tied the knots! Could you tell me, do you think?'

Know-It-All took the handkerchief and felt all the knots with a very wise look on his face. Then he took it indoors and, to Too-Hot's surprise and dismay, threw the handkerchief on to the fire. But it didn't burn. No, it simply lay there, turning blue, then green, then red, and suddenly it jumped right out of the fire and landed at Know-It-All's feet.

The brownie picked it up and rubbed it between his hands. All the knots had turned green, so the handkerchief looked a bit peculiar now. It was yellow with purple spots and green knots!

'Here you are,' said Know-It-All, handing it to

Too-Hot. 'You'll find the reason for your knots written across it.'

Too-Hot took it and looked at it. The first word, 'sunshine', had gone and in its place was written 'too hot'.

'Too hot!' said Too-Hot, astonished. 'Now what does that mean? That's my name – why should that be written across the handkerchief?'

'Well, I expect you wanted to remind yourself not to let something get too hot,' said Know-It-All. 'Didn't you, now?'

'No, I don't think so,' said Too-Hot, puzzled. 'Now, let me see – what gets too hot? I don't like to let my kitchen stove get too hot – but that hasn't a fire in this summer weather. So I can't have wanted to remind myself of that. It's very difficult to find out the meaning of these four knots, isn't it, Know-It-All?'

'It seems to be,' said Know-It-All, taking up his knitting again. 'That will be a silver sixpence, please, Too-Hot.'

Too-Hot paid his silver sixpence and went off again, still worried and puzzled. He looked in his purse. He had one silver sixpence left. He would go to Dame Squeeze and see if she could tell him why he had tied four knots in his handkerchief. Then he couldn't go to anybody else because he would have spent all his money.

Dame Squeeze lived in the middle of Ho-Ho Wood. Too-Hot made his way there and knocked at her front door. Dame Squeeze opened it and told Too-Hot to come inside.

'What do you want?' she asked. 'I'm very busy with a new spell, so don't stop long.'

Too-Hot told her what he wanted.

'That's easy,' said Dame Squeeze. 'Give me the handkerchief.'

She took it and undid each of the four knots. She put a pat of butter in one corner and knotted it up again. She put a yellow feather in another corner and knotted that up. She put a dab of honey in the third corner and a fish tail in the last one. When they were all knotted up once more she stood on the handkerchief and said a few magic words.

Then she picked it up and opened it out. The handkerchief was in a terrible mess now – greasy with the butter, sticky with the honey and smelly with the fish tail.

'It's got "cap" written across it,' said Dame Squeeze, showing the handkerchief to Too-Hot. 'You must have tied those knots because of a cap of some sort.'

'But I'm sure I didn't want to remember anything about a cap,' said Too-Hot, more puzzled than ever. 'Oh dear, it's a mystery! I'm afraid I shall never know why I knotted those four knots. Thank you, Dame Squeeze. You haven't really helped me at all, but here is a silver sixpence.'

Too-Hot went home sadly, wishing he hadn't spent all his money.

'I'll have some fried potatoes for my lunch,' he

said to himself. 'I can't buy anything because I haven't any money.'

He took a dish of potatoes and went into the garden to peel them. He sat down in the sunshine and began. The sun was very hot on his head and he wished he had brought out a hat.

I'll make myself a handkerchief cap, he thought. *I'll put a knot in each corner and then it will make a nice sun cap for me – just like I did yesterday!*

He took out his handkerchief and stared at it. It was yellow with purple spots and green knots in the corner. It was greasy and sticky and smelt of fish.

'Oh my, oh my, oh my, what a silly stupid I've been!' poor Too-Hot cried suddenly! 'I didn't put those knots in to remember anything! I just put them in to make myself a sun cap when I was shelling peas in the sunshine yesterday! That's why the handkerchief had "sunshine" and "too hot" and "cap" written across it – and I never guessed. Oh, what a foolish person I am! And to think I've spent all my money too. Oh, it's enough to make anyone cry his eyes out!'

And Too-Hot began crying and weeping as if his heart would break, but whether he really cried his eyes right out I don't know. I shouldn't be surprised if he did, for he was too foolish for anything, wasn't he?

Caterpillar Party

Caterpillar Party

THE BIG moth sailed down to where the five caterpillars were busy eating their dinner. They were fat caterpillars, each with a fur coat on, and they ate very fast indeed.

'Hallo!' said the big moth. 'We moths are giving a party for you caterpillars tomorrow night. Would you like to come?'

'A party!' said the biggest caterpillar. 'Yes, of course we'd like to come, but why are you giving a party for *us*?'

'Well,' said the moth, waving his beautiful feelers about. 'I don't expect you know it, but one day *you* will be moths like us! And we thought we would give a party for you, and tell you how to behave when the time comes for you to be moths.'

The furry caterpillars were astonished. 'How can we change into moths?' they said. 'We have no wings. We are covered with fur. We are quite different from you!'

'I dare say!' said the moth. 'But all the same, my words will come true. You see if they don't! Well, what about this party?'

'We'd love to come!' said the caterpillars at once.

'Well, come to the big bush over there tomorrow night when the moon is full,' said the moth. 'Look out for the hedgehog, though, if he's about. He likes a meal of grubs as fat as you!'

Off flew the moth, his powdery wings taking him high in the air. He was a beautiful thing. The caterpillars watched him go. Could it be true that one day they would be as lovely as that, and fly through the air?

42

A small pixie came wandering by. The caterpillars called to him eagerly. 'Tippy! We're going to a party!'

'Really?' said Tippy. 'Well, mind you go nice and clean, with your coats gleaming. Everyone has to look his best at a party.'

He skipped off. The caterpillars looked at one another. 'Do we look nice enough to go to a party? Ought we to dress ourselves up or something? The moths do look so beautiful.'

Now that night there came a great rainstorm. The enormous raindrops battered the plants on which the caterpillars fed, and broke them. The frightened creatures found themselves on the ground in the mud. They squirmed here and there, but they couldn't get away from the rain.

'What a mess we are in!' said one, sadly. 'All covered with mud – and our fur dirty and wet. We can't possibly go to the party.'

They looked at one another. They certainly were in a dreadful mess. No party for them! Why, the moths would turn them away in disgust.

And just then who should come by again but Tippy the pixie. They called to him dolefully. 'Tippy! See what the rain has done to us! We can't go to the party.'

Tippy looked at the wet, muddy, untidy caterpillars. He scratched his head and thought hard. Then he spoke. 'Caterpillars, I could clean you and tidy you up, if you like – but you would have to give me a reward.'

'Just say what you would like and if we can give it to you, you shall have it,' said the caterpillars eagerly. 'But don't ask for gold, because we don't even know what it is, unless it is the sunshine that shines each day, and you have plenty of that yourself.'

'I'll tell you what I want,' said Tippy. 'I want your fur coats! I could clean them, and make them into fur rugs to sell to the pixies to put on their beds in the wintertime.'

There was a most astonished silence. Then the biggest caterpillar spoke in a shocked voice. 'What!

Give you the fur coats we wear? Why, they *grow* on us! We couldn't possibly do that.'

Tippy grinned. 'Well, listen – suppose a time comes when you really don't want your hairy coats – when you want to throw them away – will you give them to me then? I promise not to ask you for them unless you say you don't want them.'

'All right,' said the biggest caterpillar, cheering up. 'That's a bargain. You get us all nice and tidy for the party – and we'll let you have our fur coats if we don't want them.'

So Tippy set to work on the hairy caterpillars. He fetched his little sponge. He dipped it into a little pool of dew and wetted it. Then he sponged each muddy caterpillar very carefully to get off the mud. Soon their fur coats were quite clean again.

'Now you are very wet,' said Tippy. 'Sit out here in the sun – it's just rising, look – and see if you can get really warm and dry.'

So out they all sat. Tippy watched them. Then he

fetched his little brush, and began to brush the caterpillars' soft, dry hairs.

'Beautiful!' said Tippy, brushing away hard. 'It's a pity there's no time to curl your hairs a bit. You'd look fine. There now – that's the last one of you done. Your fur coats have never looked nicer. Stay in the sun today, and towards evening I'll give you one more brushing.'

When the caterpillars went to the moths' party they looked very neat and tidy indeed. Tippy had even parted their hairs down the middle, and squirted a little of his best scent on them. The moths thought they looked very fine indeed.

The party was lovely. There was plenty to eat, and the dew-drinks were all flavoured with nectar that the moths had drawn from flowers with their long tongues. They told the caterpillars many interesting things, half of which the long-bodied creatures could not believe.

'They said we would go to sleep for a long time and

wake up as moths,' said the fattest caterpillar, on his way home. 'What nonsense!'

'And they said that although we should go to sleep as caterpillars, with heaps of legs, a long body and no wings, we should wake up with only six legs, some fine feelers, a short body and two pairs of wings!' said another caterpillar. 'Impossible! Such things don't happen.'

They told all these things to Tippy when they next saw him. He laughed.

'Well, you never know,' he said. 'There is plenty of most peculiar magic in the world, you know. But before you go to sleep, and change into moths, I want those fur coats of yours! It's about time I had them, too. You eat so much, caterpillars, that I am sure you will burst your skins soon!'

The caterpillars certainly were eating a lot – and some of them were so fat they looked as if they might burst at any moment. Then the biggest one suddenly stopped eating.

'I feel strange,' he said. 'Very strange. My skin is too tight for me. It's splitting! It is, really!'

Pop! It split down his back. 'I must get out of my skin!' cried the caterpillar. 'It's too tight. It's too tight! Help me, Tippy!'

Tippy helped him. The caterpillar wriggled and Tippy tugged. Soon the tight skin was peeling away from the caterpillar's body. It was off! There it lay beside him, a little ball of fur, a tiny fur coat that he no longer wanted.

'You've got a beautiful new hairy skin underneath!' said all the other caterpillars, staring. 'What a wonderful thing!'

'Of course he has!' said Tippy. 'I've seen caterpillars doing this for years! Hurry up and split your coats, you others. I want the skins to make into fur rugs. Don't forget your bargain with me.'

Well, of course, the other caterpillars soon got so fat that their skins split too, and you should have seen Tippy pulling and tugging at them, and the caterpillars wriggling. Soon the pixie had a fine hoard of furry skins in his cottage. The caterpillars were only too pleased to let him have them. They all had beautiful new furry coats, under their old skins!

And dear me, those coats split too as soon as the caterpillars grew too fat for them! Tippy was always there when that happened, you may be sure, and he rolled up the cast-off fur coats, put them on his shoulder and marched off with them.

One day the caterpillars could eat no more. They began to weave themselves silken beds, and they went to sleep inside these. They were too sleepy even to say goodbye to Tippy.

But he said goodbye to them. 'I'll see you when you wake up!' he said. 'And you'll see what a fine little shop I have then, with fur rugs of all kinds hanging up for sale!'

He was soon very busy. He cut each furry coat and trimmed it so that it made an oblong rug. He washed each one carefully and set it to dry in the sun. Then he brushed the fur well.

After that he hired a tiny shop and hung up the rugs for sale. The very small ones were for the pixie cots or prams. The bigger ones were for beds. And how the little folk hurried to buy them!

'Such beautiful rugs! As warm as can be! Wherever did Tippy get them? Tippy dear, what fur is this? What animal gave you his skin for these lovely rugs?'

But Tippy wouldn't tell his secret. No, he wasn't going to have anyone sharing such a fine secret!

One day the caterpillars in the silken cocoons woke up. They crawled out of their cosy beds and looked around. They stared at one another in surprise.

'We're different! We've got wings! We're moths!'

So they were. They spread their soft, powdery wings and flew off into the night air, rejoicing. It had been nice to be greedy caterpillars – but oh, how much nicer to be moths, with wings like the little folk, and with a long tongue that could pierce to the heart of a flower and drink the sweet nectar hidden there!

They went to see Tippy. He showed them his fine collection of fur rugs. 'See?' he said. 'You didn't want them but I did! They will keep many a pixie and elf warm in the winter nights. How different you look, moths! Magic has been at work on you – powerful magic!'

It's strange, isn't it, that caterpillars throw away their coats when they grow too big for them? Have you ever found one, rolled up and cast away? Perhaps Tippy has been before you and taken each one. Clever little thing, isn't he?

Mr Twiddle
Fetches Polly

Mr Twiddle
Fetches Polly

'TWIDDLE, YOU'RE not listening to what I'm saying!' said Mrs Twiddle.

'Yes, I am, dear,' said Twiddle, without looking up from his paper. 'I like listening to you. You go on and on like a dear little brook, and—'

'Twiddle! A brook doesn't ask questions and I do!' said Mrs Twiddle. 'Will you please answer that I've just asked you!'

'Oh – did you ask me something?' said Twiddle in surprise. 'What was it?'

'Now, Twiddle – I've been telling you about Polly, who's living with Miss Pepper at Grey Roofs,' said Mrs Twiddle.

'Oh, yes, yes – of course!' said Twiddle, who hadn't heard a word about Polly.

'And I told you I wanted you to go and fetch her and bring her here,' said Mrs Twiddle. 'I've said I'll let her stay with us for a day or two while Miss Pepper is away – now don't tell me you didn't hear a word!'

'I wouldn't dream of telling you anything of the sort!' said Twiddle. 'Of course I'll fetch Polly. How old is she?'

'I've no idea,' said Mrs Twiddle. 'She won't be very big. She's got a lot to say for herself, Miss Pepper tells me, so it will be fun to have her here for a day or two. She's a proper chatterbox!'

Mr Twiddle quite forgot that he had to go and fetch Polly that morning, and Mrs Twiddle, who thought he had gone long since, was very cross when she saw him sitting in the garden. She put her head out of the window.

'Twiddle! There – you've forgotten to fetch Polly!

I knew you would!'

'No, I haven't! I'm just going!' said Twiddle, and leapt to his feet. He hurried indoors to get his hat and stick.

'Now, you know where to go, don't you?' called Mrs Twiddle. 'I think I'd better write it down for you, Twiddle. Miss Pepper at Grey Roofs – now, where's my pencil?'

'I can remember a simple thing like that, thank you!' said Twiddle, and walked off in a huff. Good gracious, anyone would think he couldn't even go and call for a little girl called Polly without having it all written down for him! Really, Mrs Twiddle was treating him like a donkey!

He went off down the road, swinging his stick crossly. But the sun was nice and warm, and he soon forgot to be cross. He went up the hill and made his way to a little lane. He came to a house with a name on the gate. Ha! – Green Roofs – this was where Polly lived. Now he must go in and ask for Miss Pepper and get Polly. He went in and knocked at the door. A little maid answered it.

'Good morning,' said Mr Twiddle, politely. 'Is Miss Pepper at home?'

The little maid giggled. 'You've made a mistake,' she said. 'It's Miss Salt that lives here, sir.'

'Dear me – how stupid of me!' said Twiddle, thinking that he had mixed up pepper and salt. 'I mean Miss Salt, of course.'

'She's out, sir,' said the little maid. 'Can I give her a message?'

'Well – I've come to fetch Polly,' said Twiddle. 'Is she ready to come?'

'Oh yes!' said the girl. 'Miss Salt has already said goodbye to her. She dotes on her, you know! You won't want her cage, will you, sir?'

'Her cage?' said Twiddle, startled. 'Does she have a cage?'

'Well, of course!' said the maid. 'But she uses her perch most of the time. And she's such a talker, sir!

My, I never knew such a chatterbox!'

'Er – well, I heard she had a lot to say for herself,' said Twiddle, feeling very surprised. 'But really ...'

'Hello, hello, hello!' called a bright voice from indoors. 'Good morning, good afternoon, good night!'

'That's Polly,' said the maid, giggling at Mr Twiddle's surprise. 'I'll get her, sir. She'll sit on your shoulder all the way back. She's no trouble at all.'

She disappeared and came back with a pretty grey parrot with a red tail, whose feathers rose at the sight of Twiddle.

'Where's your hanky?' said the parrot at once and Twiddle felt in his pocket.

'Oh, you don't need to take any notice of what Polly says, sir!' said the maid. 'Why do you look so surprised?'

'Well – er – to tell you the truth I was expecting another kind of Polly,' said Twiddle. 'Made a mistake, of course. Somehow I didn't think it would be a Polly like this. Will she really sit on my shoulder?'

'Oh yes,' said the maid and put the bird on to his

shoulder. 'She'll stay there till you get back, sir. She's as good as gold – but oh, such a chatterbox!'

Twiddle said goodbye to the maid and went, walking rather cautiously in case the parrot fell off. Polly had no intention of falling, however, and dug her claws hard into Twiddle's coat.

'Hello, hello, hello!' said the parrot when they met old Mrs Trip. She was short-sighted and didn't see the parrot on Twiddle's shoulder. She was most surprised to be shouted at like that.

'Good morning, Mr Twiddle!' she said, and swept by.

'Goodbye-eee!' called the parrot, cheekily, and Twiddle felt really cross.

'Be quiet,' he said, fiercely.

'Shut up!' said the parrot at once. Twiddle decided not to have any more conversation after that. Instead, he began to feel extremely cross with Mrs Twiddle for saying she would have someone else's Polly-parrot for a few days. Oh, why hadn't he listened that morning when Mrs Twiddle was telling him all about it? Then he wouldn't have made such a silly mistake.

The parrot began to sing. 'Hush-a-bye-baby, on the treetop!' it sang, and Twiddle went red right to his ears. What a dreadful bird! Making everyone stare at him. He was very, very glad when at last he came to his own front gate.

He took the parrot indoors and shut the door. He set the bird down in the sitting room and called to his wife.

'I've brought Polly back! I've put her in the sitting room!'

And with that he hurried out into the garden to sit down with his paper again. What a bird! Well, he wouldn't go indoors more than he could help while that bird was with them!

He saw the cat sitting comfortably in his deckchair and turned it out. 'Look – you go and see who's in the sitting room!' he said. The cat turned her back on him and stalked off to the kitchen window.

Twiddle had a moment of panic. Suppose the cat attacked the bird and killed it! Goodness, what a to-do there would be! He listened in fear.

A loud voice came from the house. 'Hello, hello, hello! Puss, puss, puss! One, two, three, four, five, three cheers, hip, hip, hooray!'

And then the cat appeared again, leaping hurriedly out through the window and back into the garden, all its fur standing on end. What was that peculiar thing in the sitting room?

Mrs Twiddle, upstairs in her bedroom, was rather surprised to hear the noise downstairs. She called from her bedroom door.

'I won't be a minute, Polly! Sit down, dear, and look at a book. I'm just changing my blouse.'

'Hush-a-bye-baby, on the treetop!' sang Polly, cheerfully.

Dear little thing – singing nursery rhymes as good as gold, thought Mrs Twiddle. *It will be nice to have a child staying here for a day or two.*

'Milko!' called Polly. 'Milko! Coo-eeeee! All change, all change!' Then she whistled just like an express train.

Mrs Twiddle was rather shocked. Dear dear – to think a little girl could whistle like that! What would the neighbours say?

She went to the top of the stairs. 'Be quiet, dear!' she called. 'I'll soon be down. Be quiet, now!'

'Shut up!' said Polly, in glee. 'Bang-bang, you're dead! Pass the salt, please. Hip-hooray!'

What an extraordinary child, thought Mrs Twiddle, anxiously. *I don't think Twiddle will like her – especially if she tells him to shut up. Most impolite.*

'Good morning, good afternoon, good night!' shouted Polly. 'How-do-you-do, you'll miss your train, there it goes!' And she whistled again. Even Twiddle heard her out in the garden, and as for the cat, it shot right to the very back of the shed and hid there.

Mrs Twiddle hurried downstairs. Really, that whistle! She opened the door of the sitting room and looked around for the little girl she expected to see. She didn't notice the parrot, who was perched high up on the curtain pole.

'Polly!' said Mrs Twiddle, looking all round. 'Don't hide, dear. Where are you, Polly?'

'Bang-bang, you're dead!' said Polly from the curtain pole, and gave a squeal of laughter. Poor Mrs Twiddle nearly jumped out of her skin. She stared up at the parrot, astounded. A parrot! How did that get here – and where was the little girl she expected?

'Milko! Milko! Two pints of bread and a loaf of milk!' said the parrot. 'Bang-bang, you're . . .'

'Oh no, I can't bear it!' cried poor Mrs Twiddle, and ran into the garden.

'Twiddle, Twiddle, there's a parrot, a very rude parrot, in the sitting room, and the little girl you fetched must have been frightened and has gone! Oh, Twiddle – what shall I do about the parrot? Where did it come from?'

Twiddle stared at his wife in amazement. 'But – but – you told me to fetch Polly from Miss Salt at Green Roofs!' he said. 'And that's Polly. She's a parrot, not a girl.'

'Twiddle! I told you to fetch Polly from Miss Pepper at Grey Roofs!' said Mrs Twiddle. 'And you've brought a parrot home – a Polly-parrot! Oh, whatever shall I do with you? And how can we get rid of the parrot? I'm scared of it!'

'So am I,' said Twiddle. 'Well...'

And just at that moment a little girl walked round the back way and into the garden – a dear little girl with golden hair and a big smile.

'Oh, excuse me,' she said. 'I couldn't make anyone hear, so I've come round the back. I waited and waited at Miss Pepper's to be fetched, but nobody came, so I've brought myself. Is that all right?'

Oh, what a darling! thought Mrs Twiddle and Mr Twiddle thought exactly the same thing. Soon they were both telling Polly about the silly mistake

Twiddle had made. How she laughed!

'I'll take Polly back to Miss Salt's for you,' she said. 'I know Polly very well – she's such a cheeky parrot.'

And hey presto, she went indoors, grabbed the parrot, set her firmly on her shoulder and walked off. 'I'll be back soon!' she called.

Mrs Twiddle turned and looked at Mr Twiddle. He waited for the huge scolding he was expecting. But instead Mrs Twiddle was smiling.

'Isn't she sweet?' she said. 'And didn't she laugh about your stupid mistake, Twiddle? Oh, I am going to enjoy having little Polly to stay, aren't you?'

'My word, yes!' said Twiddle, feeling suddenly happy again. 'My word, yes! I'd rather have a hundred Polly-girls than one Polly-parrot! I'll go and meet her! I'll take her to have an ice cream! I'll buy her a doll, I'll—'

Now be careful, Twiddle – you'll have no money left soon!

The Pixie in the
Pond

The Pixie in the Pond

ONCE UPON a time there was a small pixie called Whistle. You can guess why he had that name – he was always whistling merrily! He lived with his mother and father in a little toadstool house not far from a big pond. It was a lonely house, for no other pixies lived near, and as white ducks swam on the pond there were no frogs or toads for Whistle to play with.

'I'm very lonely, Mother,' Whistle said, a dozen times a day. 'I wish I could play with the field mice. They want to show me their tunnels under the roots of the oak tree.'

'No, Whistle,' said his mother firmly. 'The last time

you went to see a mouse's nest you got lost underground, and I had to pay three moles to go and look for you. You are *not* to play with field mice.'

'Well, can I play with the hedgehog then?' asked Whistle. 'He is a good fellow for running about with me in the fields.'

'Certainly not!' said his mother. 'His prickles would tear your nice clothes to pieces. Now run out and play by yourself, Whistle, and don't worry me.'

So Whistle went out by himself, looking very gloomy. It was dull having to play by himself – very dull. He shook his head when Tiny the field mouse ran up to him and squeaked to him to come and play. He didn't go near the hedgehog when he saw him in the ditch. Whistle was an obedient little pixie.

He ran off to the pond. He liked to watch the big dragonflies there. They were nearly as big as he was.

It was whilst he was watching the dragonflies that he saw a merry little head poking out of the water nearby, watching the dragonflies too! Whistle stared in surprise. He didn't know there was anybody else near, and here was a little pixie in the pond – a pixie about as small as himself, too!

'Hallo!' said Whistle. 'Who are you?'

'I'm Splash, the water-pixie,' said the little fellow, climbing out of the water and sitting beside Whistle. 'I live in the pond with my father and mother. We only came last week. I didn't think there was anyone for me to play with, and now I've found you. What luck!'

'Oh, Splash, I'm so pleased!' said Whistle. 'My name is Whistle. We can play together every day. What shall we play at?'

'Come into the water and I'll teach you to swim,' said Splash.

'But what about my clothes?' said Whistle. 'They'll get wet.'

'Well, they'll dry, won't they?' said Splash. 'Come along! Mind that mud!'

But dear me, Whistle was so anxious to get into the water that he floundered right into the mud, and you should have seen how he looked! He was black from head to foot!

'Oh dear!' said Whistle, in dismay. 'Look at that! I'd better get out and dry myself, and then see if the mud will brush off. Come and sit by me, Splash, and I'll teach you to whistle.'

So Splash sat by Whistle in the sun, and the pixie taught his friend to whistle loudly. By the time the dinner hour came, Splash could whistle like a blackbird! Whistle's clothes were dry, but the mud wouldn't brush off. It stuck to his clothes, and was all over his face and hands too. The two pixies said goodbye and each ran off to his dinner.

Oh dear! How cross Whistle's mother was when she saw his clothes! 'You bad, naughty pixie!' she scolded. 'You have been in the pond. Take off your clothes at once. You must have a hot bath.'

'Oh, Mother, don't be angry with me,' begged Whistle. 'I have found a friend to play with. It is a water-pixie called Splash!'

'Indeed!' said his mother, pouring hot water into the tin bath. 'Well, just remember this, Whistle – you are *not* to play with water-pixies at all! You will only get muddy and wet, and I won't have it!'

'But, Mother!' cried Whistle, in dismay. 'I do so like Splash! He is so nice. He wanted to teach me to swim.'

'You'll drown before you learn to swim in that weedy pond,' said his mother. 'Now remember, Whistle, I forbid you to play with that water-pixie.'

Whistle said no more. He knew it was no use, but he was very sad. It was hard to find a friend, and then not to be allowed to keep him.

That afternoon, Whistle stole down to the pond. Splash was there, sitting in a swing he had made of bent reed. He was whistling away, having a lovely time, eagerly waiting for Whistle.

'What's the matter?' he cried, when he saw the pixie's gloomy face.

'Mother was very cross about my muddy suit, and

says I mustn't play with you,' said Whistle sadly. 'So I came to tell you. After this I shan't come down to the pond, because if I do I might see you and play with you, and I don't want to upset my mother.'

'Oh, bother!' said Splash, in dismay. 'Just as we have found one another so nicely. It's too bad!'

'Goodbye, Splash,' said Whistle. 'I'm very, very sorry, but I must go.'

Off he ran home; and just as he got there he met his father, who called to him.

'Whistle! How would you like to go for a sail on the pond this afternoon? I've got a fine little boat here that used to belong to a child.'

'Ooh, how lovely!' said Whistle, looking at the toy boat, which was leaning up against the side of the toadstool house and was even bigger than the house itself!

'Mother! Where are you?' called Whistle, in excitement. 'Are you coming for a sail, too?'

'Yes!' said his mother. So in a short time the little

family set off to the pond, Whistle and his father carrying the ship, and his mother running behind.

They set the boat on the water, and then they all got in.

It was a windy day. The wind filled the little white sail and the ship blew into the middle of the pond. What fun it was! Whistle's father guided the boat along and Whistle leant so far over that he lost his balance! Splash! Into the water he went head-first!

'Oh! Oh! Save him! He can't swim!' cried Whistle's mother in dismay. 'Oh, Whistle, Whistle! Quick, turn the boat about and save Whistle!'

But just then the wind blew so hard that the ship simply tore across the pond and left Whistle struggling in the water. Poor little pixie – he couldn't swim, and he was in great trouble.

But suddenly up swam Splash, the water-pixie. He had watched the boat setting sail, and had kept by it all the way, though the others hadn't seen him. As soon as he saw his friend fall into the water he swam up to him, and catching hold of him under the arms, he swam with him to the boat.

'Oh, you brave little fellow!' said Whistle's father, as he pulled the two of them into the boat. 'You have saved Whistle! He might have drowned! Who are you?'

'I am Splash, the water-pixie,' said Splash. 'I live in the pond. I would very much like to be friends with Whistle and teach him to swim. He has taught me to whistle like a blackbird, and my mother is very pleased. I should like to do something for him in return.'

'Oh, you are the bravest little pixie I have ever seen!' cried Whistle's mother, as she sat hugging Whistle to her. 'Please be friends with Whistle. He must certainly learn to swim. I will make him a little bathing suit, and then it won't matter if he gets wet or muddy.'

'Oh, Mother, how lovely!' cried Whistle, in delight. 'I told Splash this afternoon that I could never see him again, and I said goodbye to him, because you said I wasn't to play with him – and now he is to be my friend after all!'

'You deserve it, for you're a good, obedient little pixie,' said his father. 'Now you'd better bring your friend home to tea with you, if Mother has enough cake!'

'Oh yes, I made treacle buns this morning,' said Whistle's mother, 'and there is some new blackberry jam too. Ask your mother if you can come, Splash!'

Splash jumped into the water and swam to his cosy little home in the reeds. In a moment or two, three pixies popped their heads out of the water – for Splash had brought his father and mother.

'Thank you for the invitation,' said Splash's pretty little pixie mother. 'He will be most delighted to come. I am just going to brush his hair. Perhaps you will all come to tea with us tomorrow? We should love to have you.'

So all the pixies became friends, and now Splash

and Whistle play together all day long, and Whistle can swim just as well as Splash can; and as for Splash's whistling, well you should just hear it! The two pixies sound like a cage full of canaries!

Wagger Goes to
the Show

Wagger Goes to the Show

'MUMMY, THERE'S to be a garden party at the Hall, in the grounds, next month!' said Terry, coming in with his sister Alice and his dog Wagger. 'Can we go?'

'There's to be all kinds of fun,' said Alice. 'There's a donkey to give rides, and all sorts of competitions, and swings and ice creams. We can go, can't we, Mummy?'

'Yes, of course,' said Mummy. 'You must start saving up your money at once, then you will have a nice lot to spend.'

'And, Mummy, there's a baby show,' said Alice.

'Isn't it a pity we haven't got a baby, because then it might win a prize at the baby show. I expect Mrs Brown's baby will win. It's the fattest baby I ever saw.'

'Oh, it isn't always the fattest babies that are the best ones,' said Mummy. 'Well, I'm afraid you can't take a baby. You're my baby, Alice, and you're seven!'

'Let's put Alice in for the baby show,' said Terry with a grin.

'I'm not a baby,' she said. 'Oh, there's a dog show too. We're going to put Wagger in for that. What sort of dog is he, Mummy?'

'He's what we call a mongrel – just a mix-up of a dog. He's not pure-bred like the fox terrier next door. He's a very ordinary, rather ugly mongrel.'

'Mummy!' said both children, in horror. 'He's *not* ugly! He's beautiful.'

'Well, darlings, you think he's beautiful because he's yours and you love him,' said Mummy. 'But he isn't really beautiful. His tail is too long. He's too big. His ears aren't quite right. He'd never win a prize at a dog show.' Wagger looked up at the children and wagged his long plumy tail. They stared down at him, looking into his bright eyes.

'I didn't know he was a mongrel,' said Alice. 'I didn't know he was a mix-up dog. I thought he was the nicest dog I ever knew. I still think so.'

'So do I,' said Terry and he gave Wagger a stroke on his head. 'And I'm going to take him to the garden party even if all the dogs there turn up their noses at him! He'd hate to be left behind.'

'Well, don't put him into the dog show,' said Mummy. 'Everyone would laugh at him, he's such a peculiar-looking dog. Yes, I know he's a darling, and faithful and loving – but he *is* ugly!'

The children went out, with Wagger jumping beside them. They simply couldn't see that he was ugly at all. 'He's got the nicest eyes!' said Terry.

'And the loveliest ways,' said Alice. 'Does it matter so much that he's a mongrel? Oh dear – it's a shame he can't go in for the show.'

'Well, he may not be the most beautiful dog, but he's the happiest and healthiest,' said Terry. 'We look after him much better than they look after their dog next door.'

'Yes, we do,' said Alice. 'Wagger always has good meals and fresh water every day. And we bath him properly, and brush his coat well every morning. And he has a warm blanket in his basket, and lots and lots of walks all the year round.'

'Wuff,' said Wagger, licking Alice's hand.

'He understands every word we say,' said Alice, and she hugged him. He licked her face all over.

'Don't be upset because Mummy said you were ugly,' said Alice. '*We* think you're lovely, Wagger.'

'Wuff,' said Wagger happily. 'He wagged his long tail so fast that it could hardly be seen.

The children saved up their money that month. They ran errands and weeded the garden, and cleaned Daddy's bicycle, and whatever they were paid they put into their money boxes. Soon they had quite a lot of money.

'It's the garden party tomorrow,' said Alice to Terry one day. 'Mummy's washed my blue dress for me. And you've got new jeans to wear.'

'We ought to make Wagger look nice too,' said Terry. 'Let's give him a bath with plenty of soap and warm water. And we'll brush his coat till it shines.'

'I wish we could clean his teeth too,' said Alice.

'His teeth always look white and clean,' said Terry. 'He wouldn't like you to do that. I wish we had a new collar for him. His is old and rather dirty-looking.'

'Well, that won't matter,' said Mummy. 'He's not going in for the dog show, so he doesn't need to be all dressed up in new collars and ribbons. So long as he is clean and healthy, that's all that matters when you take him out with you. Get out the big plastic bowl if you want to wash him.'

They bathed Wagger between them. He was as good as gold. He never made a fuss about being washed like the dog next door did. He just stood in the warm water and let himself be soaped all over. He even shut his eyes so that the soap wouldn't get into them. He was as clever as that!

The children rinsed him and dried him. Then they took turns at brushing his thick, silky coat. It was rather curly, and it was fun to see the curls come up under the brush.

They even brushed his big ears and his long tail. He looked very fine indeed when they had finished with him. He capered about in delight, barking.

'I still think he's beautiful,' said Alice, looking at him. 'He's such a happy-looking dog. His eyes are so bright, and his tail is so waggy. Wagger, you're a darling!' Wagger licked her and pranced off again. He was certainly a very lively dog, always ready for a walk or a game.

Next day the children set off to the garden party, with Wagger at their heels, freshly brushed. They paid their money at the gate and ran beside the donkey all the way round the garden and back.

Then they had ice creams, and Wagger licked up all the bits that dropped on the ground. After that they went to have a swing, and Wagger waited on the ground below, because he didn't like swinging.

Then they all went to see the babies at the show, and Alice was glad she wasn't the judge, because she thought all the babies were as nice as one another. Terry didn't like them so much. He said they made too much noise, and their faces were ugly when they screwed them up to cry.

Then they had another ice cream each, and spent some money trying to fish prizes out of a pretend fish pond with a little fishing rod. But they weren't lucky, and couldn't hook a single prize! Wagger watched solemnly, and once he wuffed as if to say, 'I'm sure *I* could hook a prize if I had a chance!'

Then a bell rang, and someone called out that the dog show was about to begin. Everyone with dogs hurried to the big tent. What fine dogs there were, to be sure. Terriers dancing about on neat little legs,

Pekes, with their snub noses, looking rather haughtily around. Scotties and Sealyhams barking loudly with excitement. Really, it was all very thrilling!

'We'll go in and see the show,' said Terry. 'But we'd better leave Wagger outside, as we can't show him. It's a shame! Poor Wagger. He can't help being a mongrel.'

They tied Wagger up outside the tent and went in. There was a ring of sawdust inside, and here people walked their dogs round and round when they were showing them. The children watched, and the judges, sitting nearby, made notes and talked in low voices to each other.

Then they called out which dogs won the first prize and second prize. The fox terrier who belonged to the family next door won second prize and got a red ticket. His owner, a big boy called Ray, was delighted.

'See, Terry,' he said, as he passed him. 'I've got second prize for Nobby. Pity your dog's such an awful mongrel!'

Then one of the judges got up to speak. 'We have now awarded all the prizes for the various breeds of dog,' he said. 'But there is one special prize to come, for which any dog can be entered, whatever breed he is. This is a prize given for the best-kept and healthiest dog. Please bring your entries to the ring one by one.'

So one by one the dogs were all brought up. Ray brought his Nobby too, proudly wearing the red ticket marked 'SECOND' in his collar.

And then a dog walked into the ring all by himself! The children gasped. It was Wagger! Somehow he must have wriggled himself free and come to find Alice and Terry. He walked into the ring of sawdust, looking all round for them.

The judges thought he was entered for the competition. One put his hand on Wagger's collar and looked at his teeth. Wagger didn't mind at all. He just wagged his tail hard.

The judges ran their hands over his coat. They

looked at Wagger's eyes. They lifted up his feet and felt down his legs. Wagger barked joyfully. He thought they were making a nice fuss of him.

Wagger was the last dog in the ring. One of the judges looked round the tent and called out loudly, 'Who owns this dog? Will they please come forward?'

Rather scared, Alice and Terry went into the ring. Wagger greeted them with loud barks, licks and jumps.

'We – we didn't mean...' began Alice. But the judge interrupted her.

'Ah, so you own this lovely dog,' he said. 'Well, I am pleased to say that we shall award him the prize for being the healthiest and best-kept dog in the show. His coat, his teeth, his spirits are all first-class – a very fine specimen of a dog, and most intelligent.'

And, to the children's enormous surprise, one judge handed Terry a white ticket marked 'FIRST' in big letters, and another judge handed Alice a new collar for Wagger, and a big box of chocolates for both of them.

'Oh, thank you,' said the children, and Terry said, 'But – he's only a mongrel, you know.'

'Any dog can enter for this kind of competition,' said the judge, smiling. 'It's for the best-kept, healthiest dog – no matter what kind he is, pure-bred or mongrel. You deserve the prize for keeping your dog in such good condition.'

Wagger barked and licked the judge's hand. The children turned away in delight, and bumped into Ray, who was holding Nobby on a lead.

'We've got a First,' said Terry, beaming. 'Oh, Ray – Wagger's got a First, and Nobby's only got a Second. I've never had such a surprise in my life.'

'Let's go home now,' said Alice. 'I want to tell Mummy. Let's go quickly. And we'll give Mummy the box of chocolates, because it was she who taught us to keep Wagger so well and happy.'

So they left the garden party and tore home to

tell Mummy the good news. She was just as surprised and delighted as they were. She hugged them all – Wagger too.

'We must all share the chocolates,' she said. 'Wagger, you look fine in your new collar. Really, you look beautiful!'

'He does, he does!' said Terry. 'Three cheers for old Wagger, the best dog in the show!'

'Wuff, wuff, wuff!' said Wagger, three times, and made everyone laugh. Really, he's a very clever dog, indeed!

Plum Jam

Plum Jam

'I WISH I had some plums to make plum jam,' said Lightfoot the pixie to Prickles. Prickles the hedgehog was her neighbour. He lived under the hedge where Lightfoot had her tiny house.

'Buy some,' said Prickles.

'I haven't any money,' said Lightfoot. She never had! She left her purse about everywhere, and the little red imps were always running off with it.

'Well – go and ask Mr Frowny for some,' said Prickles. 'Go on! Take your basket with you. He's got a lot of plum trees, and there are quite a lot of plums on the ground. He doesn't even bother to pick them up!'

'Oh, I daren't ask him,' said Lightfoot. 'He's always so cross, and he's got such dreadful eyebrows to frown with. I wouldn't ask him for anything. You go, Prickles. Can't you go for me? If you will, I'll give you a pot of my plum jam all for yourself. You can spread it on the toadstools you like to eat so much and make a meal of toadstool and jam. Lovely!'

'It does sound nice,' said Prickles. 'Well, I'm not afraid of Mr Frowny. He can waggle his big eyebrows at me all he likes, and I shan't mind a bit!'

'All right, then – you go along,' said Lightfoot. And Prickles ran off, his little bright eyes looking round and about for slugs as he went. He liked a meal of slugs. He thought they were even nicer than beetles.

He came to Mr Frowny's house. Mr Frowny was in his garden, weeding. Prickles ran up to him. 'Please, Mr Frowny, may I have some of your plums?'

'What! Do you think you can climb trees and pick plums?' said Mr Frowny.

'Oh no. But I could take some of those that are on the ground,' said Prickles.

'And how many could you take in that little mouth of yours?' said Mr Frowny. 'You need your legs to run with, so you can't carry any with those. Ho, ho! You could only take half a plum, Prickles!'

'Well, may I go and take some, Mr Frowny?' asked Prickles. 'Please say yes. I'll do you a good turn, if you like, in payment.'

'And pray what good turn can you do me?' asked Mr Frowny, waggling his enormous eyebrows to scare Prickles.

But Prickles wasn't a bit scared. 'Please, sir, I will come and gobble up all your slugs,' he said. 'They feast on your lettuces, don't they? Well, I'll save your lettuces if I eat up all your slugs!'

'Very well,' said Mr Frowny. 'You can go and take as many plums as you can carry – but you'll only be able to carry half a plum in that silly mouth of yours. Ho, ho, ho!'

Prickles ran off. He went into the orchard, and he looked for a plum tree. Ah, there was one, a nice early tree, thick with little round red plums. Lovely!

Prickles ran to the tree. There were such a lot on the ground. Did he pick them up in his small mouth, or try to carry some off in his front paws?

No, he had a much better idea than that! What do you think he did? He curled himself tightly into a ball of prickles, and then he rolled himself round and round and round under the plum tree, among all the fallen plums.

What happened? Why, a great many plums stuck to his prickles! When he uncurled himself at last there were the plums, sticking all over him.

He ran out of the gate, and Mr Frowny saw him. He stared in surprise. 'Hey! What's the matter with you? You do look odd! My goodness me – you're stuck all over with plums! So that's how you're going to take them away. Come back!'

But Prickles didn't come back. He scuttled down

the lane, into the field, and ran down the hedge till he came to where Lightfoot was sewing outside her little house. She jumped up with a squeal.

'Oh! Whatever's this! Gracious – it's you, Prickles – but what have you done to yourself?'

'Brought you some plums to make plum jam, of course,' said Prickles proudly. 'Aren't I clever? Now you just take them all off my prickles one by one, Lightfoot, and wash them. Then get out your sugar, ready to make jam. You will be able to make a nice lot!'

'You clever little thing!' cried Lightfoot. 'I'd kiss you if there was anywhere to kiss!'

'There's my nose,' said Prickles. 'But I don't much like being kissed. I'd rather have a pot of jam.'

'You shall have one!' said Lightfoot, pleased. 'I'll make you some straight away, and we'll have it for tea. You must come to tea with me today.'

She set to work to make the jam. Soon it was bubbling on the little stove, smelling very good indeed. Prickles sniffed hard. It would be very nice to spread on toadstools!

He went to tea with Lightfoot that afternoon. Outside her tiny house grew a little ring of toadstools. Prickles spread some plum jam on the top of one, and then nibbled it all round the edge till it was gone.

'Delicious!' he said. 'Best I ever tasted. Thank you very much, Lightfoot.'

'Now you take this pot away with you, and you can spread plum jam on your toadstools every day,' said Lightfoot. 'You deserve it for your cleverness!'

Prickles kept his word to Mr Frowny. He ate all his slugs for him, and now Mr Frowny has the finest lettuces in the town. So, you see, everybody was pleased!

The Train That
Lost Its Way

The Train That
Lost Its Way

THE NURSERY was dull and quiet. The children had gone away to the seaside, and there was nobody to play with the toys.

'There's nothing to do!' said the toy clown.

'I'm bored,' said the teddy bear. 'I don't even want to growl any more.'

'Well, that's a good thing,' said the big doll. 'I don't like your growl.'

The bear at once growled loudly. He just did it to annoy the big doll, not because he wanted to.

'Mean thing,' said the big doll, and they began to quarrel.

'You know, something must be the matter with us,' said the toy panda, looking at everyone out of his big black eyes. 'We are always quarrelling. Yesterday the clown pulled my tail.'

'And this morning the bear threw my key across the room,' said the clockwork mouse.

'And the clown smacked the big doll,' said the bear. 'Yes, something must be the matter with us.'

'I know what it is,' said the panda. 'We want a holiday! The children go away for holidays, the grown-ups go away – yes, even Topsy the dog goes away – but we don't.'

'What's a holiday?' asked the clockwork mouse.

'Isn't he a baby?' said the big doll. 'A holiday, silly, is when you leave your home and go and stay somewhere else for a change. And you come back feeling much better and you don't quarrel any more.'

'Then I should like a holiday,' said the clockwork mouse. 'Let's go and get one!'

All the toys began to feel excited. Yes, it would be

great fun to go away for a holiday. But where should they go?

'To the seaside!' said the big doll.

'What's the seaside?' asked the clockwork mouse. 'Is it a kind of seesaw?'

'Of course not, baby!' said the big doll. She thought for a bit. She had never been to the seaside and she really wasn't quite sure what it *was* like.

'You'll see when you get there,' she told the clockwork mouse.

'Well, that's settled, then,' said the clown. 'We shall go away for a holiday – and we shall go to the seaside. Hurrah!'

'How do we go?' asked the bear.

'Well – the children went by train,' said the panda. 'I heard them say so.'

'Then *we'll* go by train!' said the bear. 'Where's the old wooden train? Oh, there you are. Train, will you take us to the seaside in your trucks? Do say yes. I'm sure you want a holiday too.'

'Yes, I'll take you,' said the wooden train, and it trundled up to the toys. 'I don't know the way, but we can ask. Get in.'

'What! Are we going *now*?' said the big doll. 'Gracious, I must pack.'

'What's pack?' asked the clockwork mouse. But nobody took any notice. The big doll got a bag and stuffed a lot of things into it. Then she hurried the clockwork mouse towards the wooden train.

'Get in,' she said. 'It's time we were off.'

'I'll be the guard,' said the clown, and he took a little green flag from the toy cupboard. He got into the last truck and beamed round at everyone.

'I'd better have a driver,' said the wooden train. 'I can go by myself all right, round and round the nursery, but I'd rather have a driver if we are going a long way.'

'I'll be the driver,' said the teddy bear. 'I've always wanted to be an engine-driver. Now, is everyone ready?'

THE TRAIN THAT LOST ITS WAY

The wooden train had three trucks, all of different colours. There was plenty of room in them. The panda, the pink cat, the monkey and the wooden soldier got into the first truck. The big doll, the little doll and the clockwork mouse got into the second truck.

The clown was in the last truck with the blue rabbit. They were great friends and always went everywhere together.

'Ready?' said the clown. 'Right away, then!' He waved his green flag and he blew the whistle. The wooden train, feeling very grand to have a driver and a guard, rumbled over the carpet to the door. They were off!

Out of the door went the train, and down the passage. The garden door was open and the train rattled down a little step, almost upsetting itself as it went.

'Hey! Be careful!' yelled the bear. 'I almost fell out.'

Down the garden path went the train at top speed. It was really enjoying itself. It scared two sparrows into the air and made the cat jump on top of the wall in a great hurry. Then it came out into the lane at the bottom of the garden.

'Stop a minute,' said the bear. 'Which way do we go?'

The train stopped. The monkey saw a swallow flying in the air and called to it.

'Hi, swallow! You fly over the sea and back every year. Which way to the seaside, please?'

'Take the road to the south,' twittered the swallow. 'Down the lane, that way.'

So off the train clattered again, scaring old Mrs Brown terribly when it met her in the lane.

'Now what could that have been?' she said. 'A red snake? No, there isn't such a thing.'

Down the lane and round the corner and into the wood. 'Keep to the path, wooden train, or we'll all be jerked out!' cried the bear. 'It's so bumpy off the path.'

The train was now on a little rabbit-path – and dear me, the path led right to a rabbit hole! The train didn't stop when it came to the hole – it rushed straight down it!

It was dreadfully dark in the burrow. All the toys yelled out in fright. 'Where are we going? Stop, train, stop!'

'It's all right!' shouted the train. 'It's only a tunnel. Didn't you know that trains ran through tunnels? We'll soon be out in the open again. Don't worry, now, we shall soon be out in the sunshine.'

But, of course, they went deeper and deeper down, and very soon the wooden train and all its passengers were quite lost.

The teddy bear made the train stop. 'We'll be in the middle of the earth if you go on like this,' he said. 'Now, look – here comes a rabbit. We'll ask him the way.'

The rabbit was very surprised to see the train down the burrow. 'Trains aren't allowed down here,' he said. 'You'd better go back.'

'Can't,' said the train. 'I can only go forward.'

'Well, if you go on you'll come to Toadstool Town,' said the rabbit. 'The pixies live there. They will tell you the way to go if you ask them.'

So on went the train again at top speed, along the dark tunnel. Then, quite suddenly, out it came into the sunshine.

'Dear me, how bright it seems!' said the big doll, blinking. 'Teddy bear, I don't think much of you as a driver. I'm sure this isn't the way to the seaside.'

All round them were big toadstools. The little doll was excited to see them, because she was small enough to knock at the door of one!

'It's a little house!' she said. 'Look, it's got a door in the stalk – and a tiny stairway goes up to the top.'

The pixies came crowding round the train. It was panting and puffing with its quick run.

'Stop here and have a meal with us,' said the pixies to the toys. 'Then we will tell you the way to the seaside.'

So all the toys sat down and had a lovely meal with

the pixies. The little doll tried to get one of them to give her a pair of wings, but she wouldn't.

'You might buy a pair in the next town, where there is a market,' she said. 'Mine wouldn't fit you.'

'Time to get on,' said the wooden train, feeling tired of staying still. 'All aboard, please!'

'Listen – I'm the guard, not you,' said the clown. '*I* have to say that. Now – is everyone ready? Off we go again!'

And off they went, this time to the next town, where there was a market. Everyone wanted to buy something.

It was a brownie market. The little doll didn't much like the look of some of the long-bearded brownies. But she got out of the train with the rest.

As soon as the brownies saw the little doll they loved her. 'Catch her!' they cried. 'We'll keep her here with us. Stay here, little doll, and you shall have a new dress and a pair of wings and a lovely ring.'

'No, no!' cried the little doll, and she ran away.

But the brownies ran after her, and goodness knows what would have happened if the wooden train hadn't suddenly rushed at the brownies, and knocked them over like skittles.

The toys piled themselves quickly into the trucks. The clown waved his flag and blew his whistle, and the train rattled off at top speed. The brownies couldn't possibly catch it.

'I didn't buy any wings, after all,' wept the little doll. 'Oh dear, I was so frightened.'

'Sit on my knee,' said the big doll. 'You will be all right when we get to the seaside.'

But dear me, the train had been in such a hurry to leave the brownies behind that it had taken the wrong road, and had now lost itself again.

It came to an enormous hill. 'You can't climb this, train!' said the teddy bear. But there was no other way to go.

So up the hill puffed the little wooden train, dragging the trucks behind it. And at last it came to the top.

There was a pretty little cottage there, and the toys wanted to stop and ask the way of the kind-looking old woman at the gate.

But as soon as the train ran over the top of the hill it began to rush downwards and couldn't stop!

'Stop, stop!' yelled the bear, as they went faster and faster and faster. But it was quite impossible to stop, and the toys all clutched the sides of their trucks and wondered what was going to happen.

'There's a big pond at the bottom of the hill,' groaned the bear. 'We shall run straight into it, and sink to the bottom!'

'I want to get out!' wailed the clockwork mouse. 'I don't like going so fast.'

But SPLASH! Into the water they went. Everybody expected to sink to the bottom, and get soaking wet.

But the engine and trucks were made of wood, so of course they all floated beautifully. The trucks sailed along like little boats!

'Good gracious, whatever next!' said the big doll. 'Rushing down tunnels, escaping from brownies, panting up hills, tearing down them, sailing on ponds! What behaviour!'

There were some big white ducks on the pond. They didn't like the train splashing into their pond at all. They sailed up, quacking angrily.

'Peck that monkey! Peck that bear! Peck that mouse!' they cried. But the panda pulled up a reed growing in the pond and began to lash out at the big ducks.

'Go away or I'll whip you!' he said. '*Grrrrrrrrrr*!'

The ducks sailed a little way away. 'Let's make big waves and upset them,' said one duck. So they made big waves – but the waves took the engine and the trucks to the shore, and soon the train was on dry land once again.

'Thank goodness,' said the big doll. 'Now, train, do try to go slowly and don't get us into trouble any more.'

The train was wet and cold and rather tired. So it did go slowly. It went on and on and at last ran over something yellow and soft.

'What is this stuff? It looks like sand,' said the bear. 'Better get out of it, train, or your wheels will sink into it and you won't be able to move.'

That was just what did happen. The wheels sank into the sand, and the train felt too tired to drag them out. So there it stood, quite still.

The toys got out. 'I wonder where we are?' said the clown to the rabbit. 'What's the noise?'

Now, although the toys didn't know it, they had come to the seaside. They were on the sandy beach, and far down it was the sea. The tide was out, but it was just coming in.

The toys could hear the sound of the waves breaking, but they didn't know what it was. They all wandered about, picking up shells and bits of seaweed.

'This seems a very lonely kind of place,' said the monkey. 'And look, what is that far away down the sand? Is it water?'

'Yes. Another pond, I expect,' said the pink cat. 'Well, I'm not going near it. I feel tired. I'm going to go and rest against a truck. You'd better come with me.'

So all the toys went to rest themselves against the trucks, and they fell asleep. And of course the tide came in and the waves came nearer and nearer!

One wave made such a noise that it woke the monkey. He sat up in alarm.

'Look!' he said. 'That pond has come near to us. It's got waves at the edge. It's trying to reach us!'

'It's getting nearer and nearer!' cried the teddy bear, and he jumped up. 'Oh, it's a most *enormous* pond. I've never seen one like it. It's trying to swallow us up!'

Splash! A big wave broke near them and ran right to the big doll's feet. It wet her toes and she screamed.

'Quick! Let's run away!' she cried. 'We'll be

swallowed up by the waves if we don't.'

The bear, the monkey and the clown pulled hard at the train to make it run over the sand. At last they managed to get it to a firmer patch where the wheels did not sink in.

'Now, get in, everybody!' cried the bear. 'We're off!'

Splash! A wave ran right up to them and the train rushed away in fright. It tore up the beach and on to the roadway. It rattled along, with all the toys holding tight. Dear, dear, where would they get to next?

After a long, long time they came to a little town. The train rushed down the street, and came to an open gateway. It ran in, panting.

'I really must have a rest,' it said. 'Get out, toys, for a minute.'

They got out – and the big doll gave a loud cry. 'Why – we're in our own garden! Look – there's the rosebed – and the garden seat – and the children's swing! Train, you've brought us all the way back. However did you know?'

'He didn't,' said the bear. 'It was just good luck. My goodness, I'm glad to be home again. No more holidays for me!'

'I *should* have liked to see the seaside,' said the clockwork mouse, as they all went back to the nursery.

'So should I,' said the big doll. 'We'll go another day.'

'But not by train,' said the monkey. 'We'll go on the rocking horse. He's not so likely to lose his way!'

'Well, I did my best,' said the wooden train. 'I couldn't *help* losing my way. The teddy bear should have taken me the right way!'

'Never mind – it was a most exciting journey,' said the bear. And it certainly was, wasn't it?

The Bee Is A Busy Postman

The Bee Is A Busy Postman

A BEE stood on a stalk and cleaned his front legs carefully. A small lizard looked up and saw him.

'Bee!' he said. 'Come down and talk!'

'Too busy,' said the bee.

'Busy! You're not! Why, you do nothing but suck nectar!' cried the lizard. 'I'll come up the stalk and snap at you if you tell stories like that!'

'Well, I shall sting you if you do,' said the bee. 'I'm telling you the truth. I'm too busy to play with you. My friends and I are the flowers' postmen. We are kept very busy delivering for the flowers all day long.'

'What do you deliver?' said the lizard in wonder. 'Letters?'

'No, you silly lizard! We deliver the pollen from one flower to another!' said the bee, importantly. 'Didn't you know that? Flowers can make seeds by themselves, it is true, but didn't you know that most of them employ us as postmen, and get us to deliver the pollen to their neighbours for them?'

'Well, I never knew that before,' said the lizard. 'How do you carry the pollen from one flower to another, bee? Have you a bag or a box or something?'

'No. The flower spills its pollen on my back or my head, or wherever it likes,' said the bee. 'Come and watch, if you like. Look, I'm going into this flower, quite cleaned up – watch what I'm like when I come out!'

He squeezed himself into a flower. When he came out he was dusted with golden pollen all down his back! The lizard laughed.

'You look like a very dusty bee now,' he said. 'Go

into another flower and let me see what happens then.'

The bee squeezed into another flower. The lizard peeped in to see what happened. He saw that the pollen was rubbed off against the seed box of the flower, and that some of the tiny grains were left there.

'Did you see that?' asked the bee, coming out backwards on to the lizard's nose. 'I've delivered some pollen there. Now that flower can begin to make seed. It's a clever idea, isn't it?'

'Oh yes!' said the lizard. 'Very clever! I didn't know that before. But, bee – how very, very, very kind of you to work so hard for the flowers! I suppose you don't get any wages at all?'

'Of course I do,' said the bee. 'You don't suppose I'd work for nothing, do you? No, the flowers pay me and all the other bees very well indeed. They make nectar for us, and we take it in return for our postman work. And very delicious nectar it is too!'

'Give me a taste!' begged the lizard. But the bee wouldn't.

'Too *buzzzzzzzzzy*!' he buzzed, and flew off. Clever little postman, isn't he?

Blackberry Tart

Blackberry Tart

JANEY WAS very pleased because Ellen, who lived next door, had asked her and three other children to go on a blackberry picnic.

'Bring a big basket,' said Ellen. 'My mother knows a fine place for blackberries, and we are going to take tea with us. It will be great fun! We shall all bring our blackberries home, and our mothers will make us blackberry tart for our dinner next day.'

'Ooh!' said Janey, who loved blackberry tart. 'How lovely! I *shall* be excited this afternoon.'

But before the afternoon came, poor Janey had an accident. Mother had asked her to go and fetch some butter from the dairy down the road. So down she went to get it – and poor Janey fell off the kerb on to her knees and cut them very badly.

She didn't cry till she got home. Mother was very sorry indeed. She bathed her knees and bandaged them.

'Dear me, look at the butter!' Mother said. 'You fell on that too, Janey – it is a funny shape!'

That made Janey laugh – but she was soon in tears again, because Mother said she wouldn't be able to go to the blackberry picnic that afternoon.

'Darling, you can't possibly,' said Mother. 'You really couldn't walk all the way to the blackberry wood. Your knees are quite bad.'

Well, Janey begged and begged – but it wasn't any use. Mother was right about the knees. Janey couldn't walk very well, and she would never get to the blackberry wood.

'I did so want to go to the picnic,' said Janey, crying bitterly. 'I did want to bring home lots of ripe blackberries for you, Mother. Now I shan't have a blackberry tart.'

'I'll buy some blackberries and make a tart for you,' said Mother.

'They don't taste the same,' sobbed Janey.

'Now don't be silly,' said Mother. 'You shall have a nice little picnic with Angela your doll this afternoon. You can squeeze through the hedge into the field at the bottom of the garden, and I will give you a picnic basket all for yourself. You shall have tomato sandwiches, a piece of chocolate cake and four sugar biscuits.'

'Oh, I shall like that!' said Janey, cheering up, and she went to dress Angela in picnic clothes, so that it wouldn't matter if she got dirty.

Janey felt sad again when she saw the other children going off for their picnic. But Mother quickly packed her picnic basket for her, and Janey set off down the garden, limping a little because her knees hurt her. She put Angela through the hole in the hedge and then squeezed through after her with the basket.

Janey felt hungry, so she decided to have her picnic straight away. She went over to the other side of the field and sat on a grassy bank there. She undid her packet of sandwiches.

They tasted lovely. So did the chocolate cake. Janey saved the four sugar biscuits till last – and it was just as she was eating these that she suddenly saw the blackberries.

Janey stared as if she couldn't believe her eyes! On the hedge not far off grew blackberry brambles – and on these brambles were the largest, ripest blackberries that Janey had ever seen! They were thicker than she had ever seen too, growing in black clusters together.

Nobody came into that field except the farmer and his two horses, so nobody had seen the blackberries. There they were, waiting to be picked!

'Oh!' said Janey in delight. 'Look at them! I can pick enough to fill my basket! Won't Mother be surprised! Now we shall have our blackberry tart after all!'

She got up and limped over to the brambles. She began picking as fast as she could. Some of the berries went into her mouth – and they *were* delicious! But most of them went into the basket.

When the basket was almost full and quite heavy, Janey squeezed back through the hedge and into her own garden again. She went up to the house and called Mother.

'I'm in the front garden!' cried Mother. So Janey went there – and just as she got there all the other children came running home with their baskets of blackberries.

'Hallo, Janey!' they cried. 'It *was* bad luck that you couldn't come blackberrying with us! Look what we've got!'

'And look what I've got!' said Janey proudly, and she showed them her basket full of the big ripe berries.

'Good gracious!' said Ellen. 'They are far better

than ours! Wherever did you get them?'

'Mother let me have a picnic all to myself in the field at the back,' said Janey. 'And whilst I was having it I saw these blackberries. Aren't I lucky?'

'You *are*!' said all the others. 'Oh, Janey, we wish we'd been with you, instead of in the blackberry wood. Your berries are far bigger than ours.'

'Well, it was a good thing I fell down after all,' said Janey. 'It's funny how bad things turn into good things sometimes!'

'It depends how you behave about the bad things,' said Mother with a laugh. 'If you'd been silly and sulky about not going on the picnic with the others, and hadn't gone off by yourself to the field, you'd never had found the lovely big blackberries. Well, I'll make you a fine tart tomorrow.'

She did – a big juicy one, full of the ripe blackberries. Janey is going to eat it with cream. I wish I could have a slice, too, don't you?

Gillian and Bobs
Have an Adventure

Gillian and Bobs
Have an Adventure

ONE VERY sunny morning Gillian's mother said that Bobs could go with Gillian for a little walk in the fields. So Gillian whistled for Bobs – she was quite good at whistling – and the two of them set off down the lane.

When they had gone a little way they came to a little white gate that led across the fields. So Gillian climbed over it, and Bobs squeezed under it, and there they were in the grass that was thick with daisies and buttercups!

Gillian sang loudly and Bobs barked madly. It was such a lovely morning that they both felt they really must make a noise. They ran races – but Bobs always won, no matter how fast Gillian went. Gillian picked a bunch of daisies to take home to Katie, her little sister. Bobs found an old rat hole and began to dig so hard that the earth and grass flew up in the air all over Gillian!

'Don't, Bobs!' she cried. But Bobs went on and on, so Gillian ran away from him and hid behind a bush. Bobs was good at playing hide-and-seek. Gillian watched him digging and digging, and then at last he got tired of it. He put his nose up and looked around for Gillian.

'Wuff!' he said.

Gillian didn't say a word. She just crouched down behind the bush so that not even the top of her golden head showed.

Bobs cocked both his ears up and stared all round in surprise. Where in the world could she have disappeared to? It was most mysterious!

'Wuff, wuff, WUFF!' he barked, which meant,

'Come along, Gillian, and show me where you are.'

But Gillian didn't move, though she badly wanted to laugh. Bobs had such sharp ears she knew that he would hear even the smallest giggle. Then Bobs put his nose to the ground to smell where Gillian's feet had been and he ran round and round a few times, sniffing hard. At last he found where Gillian's shoes had walked, and he followed the smell of them with his nose.

He went across the grass – he went through a clump of buttercups – he came to Gillian's bush – and then, with a loud bark he threw himself on her and the two of them rolled over and over and over!

'I've found you!' barked Bobs.

'Yes, you have,' said Gillian. 'Now it's your turn to hide!'

But Bobs had just caught sight of something that put hide-and-seek quite out of his head! He had seen a rabbit bobbing up and down by the stream! A rabbit!

'Wuff!' cried Bobs, in delight, and he shot after

the rabbit. He went so fast that Gillian couldn't possibly catch him up. She was quite cross with him.

'Bobs! Don't play with rabbits now! Play with *me*!' she cried. But Bobs didn't come back.

'I shall go on without you, Bobs!' called Gillian, and she climbed over the stile that led into the next field. Still Bobs didn't come. So Gillian went on by herself. The buttercups were like a carpet of gold everywhere. The bees hummed, and on the hawthorn hedges the white May blossom lay like dazzling snow. It smelt very sweet, too. Gillian forgot about Bobs as she danced through the buttercup field.

She went down a little path that led to the river, and came back home another way. Her mother was picking flowers in the garden.

'Hello, dear!' she said. 'Where's Bobs?'

'Oh, hasn't he come home?' said Gillian, in alarm. 'Oh, Mummy! He went after a rabbit and wouldn't come with me – so I left him, thinking he would come home by himself.'

'Well, he hasn't,' said Mother. 'Never mind, I expect he's halfway down a rabbit hole by now. He'll come back home when he's tired of being laughed at by rabbits he can't reach.'

But Bobs didn't come home. Gillian called and whistled, and she and Mother went to the gate a dozen times to look for him, but there was no sign of him at all.

'Naughty little dog!' said Mother. 'Sandy! Sandy! Come here. You must come with us and look for Bobs.'

Sandy was the other dog that lived at the farm. He had a sandy head and a very good nose for smelling. He came running up.

'We've lost Bobs,' said Gillian. 'You must help us to find him, Sandy.'

'Wuff! Wuff!' said Sandy, wagging his tail fast. He ran down the lane with Mother and Gillian. They came to the white gate. Gillian climbed over it, Sandy squeezed under it, but Mother opened it and went through it. Sandy ran all over the field with his nose to the ground.

Suddenly, Mother, Gillian and Sandy lifted their heads and listened.

'I can hear Bobs barking!' said Gillian, in great astonishment.

'Yes, but it's such a funny bark!' said her mother. 'It sounds so far away – sort of muffled – as if he were underground or something.'

'Oh, Mummy, do you think he's managed to get right down a rabbit hole and can't get back again?' cried Gillian, with tears in her eyes.

'Of course not,' said her mother. 'He is much too big to get down a rabbit hole. Listen!'

So they all listened again – and then Sandy set off at a great pace to the streamside. He came to a tree, and began to scrape his paws against it, barking all the time!

Gillian and her mother hurried over to the tree too. It was an old, old willow tree – and inside it, deep down, they could hear poor Bobs barking!

'Look,' said Mother, pointing to the tree trunk, 'Bobs went up the tree – and down through this crack – and fell into the hollow below and couldn't get out! I expect a rabbit went that way and he thought he could too!'

'Oh, Mummy, we were playing hide-and-seek, and Bobs meant to hide from me,' said Gillian. 'Oh, I do think he's clever to choose such a good place! Bobs! Bobs! We're going to rescue you!'

'Woof, wooof, woooof!' said Bobs, scrabbling about in the tree below. 'Woof!'

'How can we rescue him?' said Mother. 'He is so far down – and the hole is so small!'

But Sandy knew how to rescue Bobs! He began to scrape away at the old, old willow tree, and the trunk flew to pieces! It was no stronger than cork! Gillian broke pieces off too, and soon there was a big enough hole to look right in and see Bobs away down where the roots of the tree were!

'Woof!' said Bobs, looking up, his two eyes shining like lanterns in the darkness of the tree.

'Woof!' said Gillian. 'Silly dog! Getting yourself lost in a hollow tree! Come now – jump! The hole is big enough for me to catch you as you jump.'

Bobs jumped – and Mother and Gillian caught him and pulled him out.

'Wuff, wuff, woof, woof!' said Bobs, licking Gillian and her mother in delight, and then tearing off round the field like a mad thing to stretch his legs.

'Well, that *was* an adventure!' said Mother, as they all went home again. 'Bobs! Next time you play hide-and-seek, just choose an easier place to get out of!'

'Woof!' said Bobs, which meant, 'Certainly, mistress!'

Peter's New Shoes

Peter's New Shoes

PETER WAS proud of his new beach shoes. They were green, and on each toe there was a white piece of rubber in the shape of a little ship.

'Aren't they nice?' said Peter's mother. 'Now listen, dear, I want you to wear these little shoes on the beach as well as when you paddle.'

'Oh, why, Mummy?' said Peter. 'I do like to feel the sand with my feet.'

'I know you do,' said his mother. 'But yesterday I saw some broken glass on the beach, and I heard of a little girl who cut her foot on a piece. So I want you to keep your beach shoes on.'

'People shouldn't leave broken glass about,' said Peter. 'It makes us wear shoes when we don't want to.'

'It is very careless of people,' said Mother. 'But as I don't want you to get your feet cut, Peter, I'd like you to keep your shoes on, and to paddle in them too. Now don't forget.'

Peter loved paddling. It was fun to go splish-splashing through the tiny waves. The stones didn't hurt his feet when he had his beach shoes on. Sometimes there was sand and sometimes there were stones. He didn't mind which if he had his shoes on.

Now that afternoon Peter was on the beach with Tinker the dog.

Peter thought he would build a big castle. He soon began, and Tinker got very excited and tried to dig too, sending the sand up into the air like a shower of spray.

'Hey! Stop, stop, Tinker!' said Peter. 'That's not helping me! I don't like sand in my eyes.'

The sand was warm in the sun. Peter's feet felt hot.

He looked down at his new shoes.

'I wish I could take you off,' he said. 'You do make my feet hot.'

'Woof!' said Tinker, and put his paw on Peter's foot.

'Yes, you needn't show me that you don't wear shoes,' said Peter. 'I know it already. I really think I'll take my shoes off for a little while. If I stay just here and don't go running over the beach I shall be all right.'

So he took them off and set them neatly by his castle. Then he went on building it up, higher and higher and higher.

And do you know, by the time the castle was finished, the sea was almost up to it. Peter was so excited! He shouted for joy. 'I shall stand on top – I shall be king of the castle! Hurrah!'

He stood right on the top of his castle. He had made it very firmly indeed and patted it down well, so it was a very strong castle.

And then Peter suddenly remembered his beach shoes. 'Oh dear! I must put them on again,' he said. So he scrambled down to find them. But he must have put sand on top of them, because they couldn't be seen anywhere.

Mother came down to the beach, and shouted in surprise to see Peter's enormous castle. 'What a big one!' she cried.

'Oh, Mummy, I've lost my shoes,' said Peter in dismay, as he looked for them.

'But I told you not to take them off,' said his mother, quite cross.

'Well, my feet were very hot, and I thought if I stayed here, just in one place, it wouldn't matter if I took them off for a little while,' said Peter, going red.

'That was very naughty of you,' said Mother. 'I trusted you not to. Hurry up and find them and put them on.'

But just then an enormous wave came and ran right round the castle – *splosh*! Peter only just jumped up in time or he would have been soaked through. His mother had to run ever so far back.

As soon as the wave had gone back, Peter got down from the castle and hunted about for his shoes once more but there wasn't any sign of them at all.

'The sea must have taken them,' said the little boy sadly. 'They're not here. Tinker, can't you find them?'

But Tinker couldn't, though he hunted too. Soon the sea was so far up the beach that Peter had to leave his castle and go and sit by the wall with his mother. She had his walking shoes with her and he put them on.

'I suppose I can't paddle in these shoes,' said Peter in a sad voice.

'Of course not,' said Mother. 'That's the worst of not doing as you are told – something horrible always happens! I am not going to punish you, because your shoes have punished you by getting lost, so that you can't paddle again.'

Peter was very upset. It was such fun to paddle.

He sat by his mother, looking very red. The sea made nice little waves and ran almost up to Peter. But he couldn't go and splash in them because he had lost his beach shoes.

Soon it was time to go home to tea. There was a little girl at the same house as Peter was staying at, and when she came in to tea her face was red with crying. Peter wondered why. But he didn't like to ask her. He thought perhaps she had lost her beach shoes too – but she hadn't, because he saw them by her spade.

'What are we going to do after tea, Mummy?' asked Peter.

'We'll go for a walk over the cliff and fly your kite,' Mother said. 'It's always so windy there.'

'Ooh!' said Peter, pleased. It was fun to fly his kite up on the cliff. The wind pulled hard and the kite flew very high.

After tea he went to speak to Mandy, the little girl. 'Where's your new bucket?' he said.

Tears came into Mandy's eyes. 'Oh, Peter,' she said,

'when I was playing with it this afternoon a big wave came and took it away. I couldn't get it back, and now it's lost. And it was such a lovely one.'

'Oh, what a pity!' said Peter. 'It was the one with Mickey Mouse on, wasn't it?'

'Yes,' said Mandy. 'I'm going to look for it on the beach after tea. Mummy says it may be left there when the tide goes down. Will you come and help me to look, Peter?'

'I can't,' said Peter. 'I'm going to the cliff to fly my kite.'

'Oh, I do wish you weren't,' said Mandy. 'If only you'd help me I'm sure I could find my bucket. But the beach is too big to look all by myself.'

Peter was a kind little boy. He badly wanted to fly his kite – but Mandy did need his help very badly too.

'Well, I'll come and help you instead of flying my kite,' he said. 'I lost my beach shoes this afternoon, so I know how horrid it is to lose something. I'll go and tell Mummy, and then we'll go to the beach together.'

So in a little while Mandy and Peter were hunting all over the beach to see if the bucket had been left by the tide. The sea had gone down, and was leaving big stretches of seaweed, shells and rubbish in crooked lines here and there. Peter and Mandy wandered up and down the long beach, looking hard.

It was dull work. Peter wished he was up on the cliff with his mother, flying his kite. He was sure he would not see Mandy's bucket. It would be just a waste of time.

But suddenly he did see it! It was under a pile of brown seaweed. He could see a bit of Mickey Mouse's red coat showing there quite clearly. He ran to it with a shout.

'I've got your bucket – I've got your bucket!' he cried. He pulled it out of the seaweed – and oh, whatever do you suppose was inside the bucket? Guess! Yes – one of Peter's green beach shoes!

'Oh! Oh!' squealed Peter in delight. 'Here's one of my shoes in your bucket, Mandy. Oh! Let's look for the other one. It's sure to be near.'

The two excited children looked hard – and soon Mandy gave a shout. 'I've got it – I've got it! Look, it's under this little rock! It's full of shells! Oh, Peter, aren't we lucky! We've found all the things we lost.'

They rushed home to their mothers. How pleased they were!

'Well, Peter, if you hadn't given up your kite-flying to help Mandy, I don't suppose either the bucket or your shoes would have been found,' said Mother, hugging him. 'So, though you were disobedient and lost your shoes, your kindness got them back. One was waiting for you in Mandy's bucket – that was funny!'

Peter always wears his shoes now, and never takes them off. So his feet are safe from glass and sharp tins. I hope yours are too!

The Little
Horse-Tricycle

The Little
Horse-Tricycle

ONE FINE sunny morning Paul went out for a ride on his little horse-tricycle. It was a nice little tricycle – a wooden horse on three wheels – and it went along quite fast when Paul pushed the pedals up and down with his feet.

Paul called the horse Spotty, because its wooden coat was painted with big, black and grey spots. It was getting rather old, and, one day, its long black tail had come out, which made Paul sad. A horse without a tail looks so strange. Paul tried to stick the tail back, but it all fell to pieces, and he had to throw it away. It was a great pity.

On this sunshiny morning, Paul thought he would ride to Bluebell Wood. So off he went, pedalling down the road and then along the green path into the wood. And it was there that his strange and exciting adventure began!

As he went down the path he suddenly came to a part of the wood he didn't know at all. Queer, crooked little houses stood in a twisty street, and there was a large-windowed shop in the middle, with the strangest bottles of sweets, the queerest cakes and funniest buns he had ever seen. Paul stopped Spotty, his horse, and looked in at the window.

Then things began to happen. A pixie, with long pointed ears, rushed up, went into the shop, snatched up a bottle of sweets and a big chocolate cake and then ran straight out again.

The shopkeeper at once appeared at the door, and shouted loudly, 'Stop thief, stop thief! You haven't paid me!'

But the pixie with the pointed ears ran off down the

street as fast as ever he could. The shopkeeper, who was a gnome with a red and yellow tunic buttoned up to his throat, danced about in rage – and then he suddenly saw Paul there, staring in surprise, sitting on his little horse-tricycle.

'After him, after him!' shouted the shopkeeper, at once. 'Go on, boy, go after him and catch him!'

The gnome jumped on to the horse behind Paul, and pushed off. Spotty the horse began to go fast, and Paul's feet flew up and down on the pedals. His hair blew out, and he gasped for breath. Spotty had never, never gone so fast before!

'There he is, the thief!' shouted the gnome shopkeeper, and he pointed ahead. Paul saw the pixie running down a hill in front of them, still carrying the bottle and the cake. On flew the horse-tricycle, faster than ever before, down the hill, and Paul began to feel quite frightened.

'Don't you think we're going rather fast?' he cried to the gnome. 'Suppose we have an accident!'

'Oh, never mind about a little thing like that!' cried the gnome. 'Go on, faster, faster, faster!'

They rushed on, down the hill and up another. The pixie in front could run really very fast indeed. Paul felt quite surprised when he saw his legs twinkling in and out. He had never seen anyone run so fast before!

Suddenly they came to a big town. It was a strange town, for all the buildings looked as if they were built of wooden toy bricks. The trees had round, wooden stands, just like toy farmhouse trees, and Paul thought they would fall over at a touch!

The runaway pixie rushed down the middle of the street. There was a small pond at the bottom, on which white toy ducks were swimming. The pixie suddenly tripped over a stone and fell sideways, splash! into the pond. The chocolate cake disappeared into the water and the bottle of sweets fell to the ground and smashed into a hundred pieces.

A wooden policeman suddenly appeared and ran to pull the pixie out of the water. Then up came Paul and the gnome on the wooden horse-tricycle, and, in their excitement, they ran straight into the pond!

They knocked the policeman and the pixie flat into the water, Paul fell in with a splash, the horse rolled on to its head and stuck there with its three wheels in the air and the gnome slid into the mud at the edge of the pond and sat there looking most surprised.

Paul climbed out and began to laugh. He really couldn't help it, everyone looked so funny. Then, up came some more policemen, and dragged everyone out – the horse-tricycle too.

'Now then, what's all this?' said the biggest policeman of the lot, taking out a large notebook.

The gnome brushed the mud off himself and explained about the robber-pixie, and how Paul had been kind enough to go after him on his tricycle. The pixie began to cry and was marched off between two of the policemen.

Paul looked in dismay at his horse-tricycle. It was very muddy and very wet. He himself was the same.

Whatever would his mother say when he went home?

The gnome saw him looking unhappy and patted him gently. 'Don't worry,' he said. 'I'll take you to my aunt's. She lives nearby, and she will dry our clothes for us and brush off all the mud. As for your tricycle, don't worry about that either. I'll take it to a shop I know here and they will clean it up beautifully for you.'

'I'll take it,' said one of the policemen. 'I pass by the shop.'

So off he went, wheeling the tricycle, and the gnome took Paul to a crooked little house not far away, where his aunt, a gnome just like himself, lived. She was dressed in red and yellow, with a big green shawl over her head, and had the kindest smile Paul had ever seen. She listened to the gnome's story in surprise, and then made them take off their wet, muddy things. She wrapped them up in two old coats and sat them by her kitchen fire, whilst she dried their clothes.

She gave them ginger buns and hot cocoa, and Paul enjoyed it all very much. It was most exciting to sit in Toytown with an old gnome aunt fussing over him, and a gnome shopkeeper smiling at him over a steaming cup of cocoa. What an adventure!

Soon, his clothes were dry, and after they had been well brushed, he put them on again. 'Now, what about my tricycle?' he asked. 'It is really time I went home, for my mother will be wondering where I am.'

Just then there came a knock at the door, and, when the gnome's aunt opened it, what a surprise! There stood the policeman with Paul's horse-tricycle, all cleaned up, shining bright – and whatever do you think! The horse had a brand-new long, curling tail! You can't imagine how fine it looked!

'It's got a new tail!' cried Paul, in delight. 'Oh, how splendid!'

'The man who cleaned it up thought perhaps it had lost its tail in the pond,' explained the policeman. 'So he gave it a new one, in case it had.'

'Please thank him very much,' begged Paul. 'Are you coming back with me to your shop, gnome? I really must go now.'

'Yes, I'll come,' said the gnome, and slipped on to the horse behind Paul once more. 'Goodbye, Aunt, and thank you very much!'

Paul called out the same and off they went through the crooked streets of Toytown. When they came to the gnome's shop he went inside and came out with a bag of little toffee sweets which he gave to Paul.

'Thank you for your help,' he said. 'Come and see me again some day. Follow that green path and it will take you out of the wood. Goodbye!'

Off went Paul, full of delight. A bag of sweets, a new tail for his horse – and a fine adventure to tell! What a lucky boy he was!

When he got home he told his mother all about his adventure in the wood, and at first she smiled and wouldn't believe him. But when she saw the splendid new tail on the horse, and tasted one of the gnome's toffee sweets, she changed her mind.

'Well, it *must* be true!' she said. 'How exciting for you, Paul! Do let's go and see the gnome one day soon.'

So they are going next Wednesday – and I wish I was going too, don't you?

Paying It Back

Paying It Back

THERE WAS once a dog called Mack. He was a little dog with a big bark, and everyone was very fond of him. He lived with Terry and Clare and they took him for a walk each day.

They were good to Mack. They always saw that he had plenty of good food to eat, and filled his bowl full of fresh water each day. They brushed him well every morning, and made quite sure that he had clean blankets in his basket.

Terry and Clare had two pets. One was Mack and the other was a big goldfish called Rudolf. Rudolf had lived in the living room ever since the children could remember. He had a very big round glass bowl, with some pondweed in it, and he swam round and round the bowl and looked at the children through the glass.

He knew Mack the dog very well indeed, for he had seen Mack brought into the house when he was a tiny puppy, so small he could hardly walk. The goldfish had looked and looked at the puppy. He had never seen one before, and he wondered what it was.

When Mack grew older he wanted to see the goldfish properly. The glass bowl was always put in the middle of the table so that the children could see the big red fish swimming whilst they were having their meals. He looked lovely peeping at them between the pondweed in the bowl. When the children fed him he popped his red nose out of the water and ate the food greedily. He would take some from the children's hands, so you see he was really very tame.

One day Mack jumped up on the table to have a good look at Rudolf the fish. He lay down on the table with his nose close to the bowl and watched the goldfish. Then he wuffed to it.

'Why don't you come out and play with me?'

'Because I should die if I left the water for long,' said the goldfish, poking his nose out of the top of the bowl to speak to Mack.

'It must be dull swimming round and round in your bowl,' said Mack.

'I have plenty to look at,' said Rudolf. 'I love to see the two children, and it's fun to see you come trotting into the room too. You are a very nice dog.'

Mack was pleased. He wagged his tail so hard that it thumped the table like a drum.

'Oh, I say! What's that funny noise?' said the goldfish in alarm.

'Only my tail wagging,' said Mack. 'It's to say I'm friendly to you. Wag your tail at me, goldfish, and then I shall see that you are friends with me too.'

'I can't wag my tail like you,' said Rudolf. 'If I wag my tail it makes me swim fast and I shall bump my nose on the bowl. But I'll waggle my fins – look!'

Rudolf waggled his fins and Mack thumped his tail again. Then he heard someone coming and he jumped off the table. He was not really supposed to climb up there.

After that Rudolf and Mack were very friendly indeed. Rudolf always got excited when Mack came into the room and Mack always gave a little bark to tell Rudolf that he was pleased to see him. Once Mack even jumped up on the table and dropped a few biscuit crumbs into the water for the goldfish. Rudolf was delighted.

Now one very, very hot day somebody upset Mack's bowl of water. It always stood outside in a shady spot. Perhaps the gardener trod on it and upset it. Anyway, the water was spilt and Mack had none at all.

There was no pond in the garden. There was not

even a puddle to drink from, for the weather had been hot and all the puddles had gone.

So Mack had nothing to drink at all. He went about with his tongue hanging out, feeling so hot that he wished he could take his coat off as Terry did.

The children were out for the day, so they did not see that Mack was thirsty. Their mother was busy, and the maid never bothered about Mack anyhow. So nobody knew that the little dog was dreadfully thirsty. The sun shone down hotly, and made him more thirsty than ever.

Then evening came and the children arrived home, laughing and talking. They noticed Mack's tongue hanging out and called to him, 'Go and have a drink, silly dog!'

'Wuff!' said Mack. But they didn't understand that he was saying that his bowl was empty. They went off to bed and left Mack downstairs. Night came and the poor little dog really thought he would die of thirst. He went to the living room and lay down panting on the floor.

Rudolf the goldfish spoke to him. 'What's the matter, Mack? You look hot.'

'I am so thirsty I think I shall die!' said Mack. 'My bowl of water has been spilt and nobody has given me any more.'

'You poor thing!' said Rudolf. 'Well, come up here on my table, Mack – and have a drink out of the water in my bowl!'

'Oh, tails and whiskers, what a good idea!' wuffed Mack. 'Do you really mean it?'

'Of course,' said Rudolf. 'You are my friend, aren't you? And friends should always help one another. But leave me enough water to swim in, won't you? If you drink it all, I should die.'

'I'll leave plenty,' said Mack, and he jumped up on to the table. He put his tongue into the bowl of water and lapped it up greedily. Oh, how delicious it was! Mack had never ever tasted such delicious water.

'Leave me enough to swim in!' cried Rudolf, as the

level of the water went down and down. 'Stop! Stop!'

Mack stopped drinking. He could have drunk the whole of the water, he was so thirsty. He had left just enough in the bottom for Rudolf to lie in – it was very little indeed.

'Bones and biscuits, I hope I've left enough!' said Mack in dismay. 'Will the children fill your bowl tomorrow, Rudolf?'

'Sure to,' said Rudolf, waggling his fins to and fro. 'Don't worry about me. I'm all right so long as I keep still. There's just enough to cover me.'

'It's very, very kind of you,' said Mack gratefully. 'I can't tell you how much better I feel already. I will do you a good turn one day, Rudolf, I really will. I will pay back the good turn you have done me, I promise you.'

Rudolf laughed and made a few bubbles in the water. 'You won't be able to pay it back,' he gurgled. 'Dogs can't help goldfish!'

But Rudolf was wrong, as you will see. Not

very long after that, there came an enormous thunderstorm. It was right overhead, in the very middle of the night. The thunder sounded like wardrobes falling down the stairs – CRASH-CRASH, RUMBLE, SMASH-CRASH! The lightning flashed and the whole world was drenched with rain. The children woke up with a jump, but they liked thunderstorms, so they didn't mind a bit. They lay and waited for the lightning to light up their bedroom.

Mack growled at the storm. He was angry with it for waking him. He was lying in his basket in the kitchen, and he heard the raindrops come pelting down the chimney nearby.

Rudolf the goldfish was dreadfully frightened. *This must be the end of the world!* he thought, and he swam round the bowl like mad. The lightning came into the room and Rudolf jumped in fright. Then such a crash of thunder came that the fish leapt right out of the water! He fell on the table and wriggled there, gasping.

He couldn't get back into the bowl. He flopped about in alarm, wondering what was going to happen to him. He could only breathe when he was under the water. He would die!

He wriggled right off the table – plop! He fell on to the floor and flapped about there, jumping and gasping for all he was worth.

'Help! Help!' panted poor Rudolf. 'Water! Water!' The children did not hear him – but Mack did! Mack pricked up his ears when he heard the plop. Then he was puzzled to hear some wriggling noises on the floor of the living room and he at once ran along the hall to see what they were.

And on the carpet lay poor Rudolf, gasping for breath! 'Oh, Mack, I shall die if I don't get back into my bowl!' he panted. 'The thunder frightened me and I jumped out.'

Mack looked at the poor goldfish. He did not dare to take him into his mouth and try to put him back, for he knew his teeth would hurt him. But whatever was he to do? He couldn't leave his friend like that.

So Mack lifted up his head and began to bark. How he barked! Wuff, wuff, wuff! WUFF, WUFF, WUFF! He went on and on, and at last everyone in the house heard him and came running downstairs to see what the matter was.

And there they found Mack sitting close beside the poor goldfish, barking for all he was worth! Terry at once lifted Rudolf up and slipped him gently into his bowl of water. How thankful the big fish was! He breathed again and swam round his bowl in delight.

'Fancy! Rudolf must have jumped out with fright!' said Clare. 'What a good thing Mack knew! Aren't they kind to one another! First Rudolf lets Mack drink his water – and then Mack rescues Rudolf!'

They all went back to bed – but Mack stayed in the living room.

'I've paid back your kindness,' he said to Rudolf, with his paws on the table. 'I've paid it back, just as I said I would. It's a nice feeling!'

'Thank you,' said the goldfish, waggling his fins. 'You're a real friend, Mack. You saved my life.'

It *is* nice to pay back a bit of kindness, isn't it? I always try to if I can, don't you?

The Runaway
Shoes

The Runaway
Shoes

THERE WAS once a little girl who would keep taking her shoes off in the garden. She liked to feel the grass prickling under her toes; but her mother scolded her and told her a dozen times a day to put her shoes on.

'Alice, there are sharp stones on the path and maybe thorns or prickles in the grass,' she said. 'You might even tread on a bit of broken glass if you run down by the rubbish heap! Then you'd cut your feet badly and be very sorry for yourself.'

But Alice wouldn't obey. So her mother made up her mind to punish her.

'Alice, every time I call and see that you have no

shoes on, I shall take a penny out of your money box to give to poor children,' she said. 'Then perhaps you'll remember about your shoes.'

Alice was cross. She was saving up for a wheelbarrow, and she didn't want her money to be given away. So she sat in a corner of the garden and sulked.

Then the naughty little girl thought of an idea. 'I know what I'll do,' she said to herself in a whisper. 'I'll take off my shoes and put them just here, behind this stone – and as soon as Mother calls me I'll run and put them on quickly, and Mother will see me running up the garden with my shoes *on*!'

Wasn't she a deceitful little girl? Ah, but wait and see what happened!

The shoes heard what Alice had said. They were shocked, because they were good shoes, and had cost a lot of money. They wanted Alice to behave nicely.

'We know what to do,' whispered the right shoe to the left one. 'As soon as Alice takes us off we'll run away and hide! Then when her mother calls her she won't be able to find us, and she'll get into trouble for being barefooted!'

So as soon as Alice had popped them behind the stone and gone to play in her bare feet, those two shoes kicked up their heels and ran off to hide under the lilac bush. They couldn't help giggling a bit.

Presently Alice's mother called her: 'Alice! Alice! I want you!'

'Coming, Mother!' called Alice, and ran at once to put on her shoes. But, dear me, they weren't behind the stone. They were gone!

Alice hunted about, but she couldn't find them. Her mother grew angry. 'Alice! Don't you hear me calling? Come at once!'

Alice had to go – and her mother saw she had no shoes on. She was very angry. 'Well, Alice,' she said, 'you must give me a penny out of your money box please.'

So Alice had to do this, and she was sad. She ran

back down the garden – and there were her shoes just behind the stone again! They had trotted there as soon as Alice had gone up the garden. 'Perhaps she will put us on again now,' they whispered to one another.

But, you know, she didn't! She glared at the shoes and simply could *not* understand how it was that they were behind the stone after all. 'I'm sure you weren't there just now,' she said. 'Well – you just stay there now, and I'll be able to put you on in a hurry if Mother calls again.'

But you may be sure that as soon as Alice's back was turned, those two shoes hopped off again as fast as they could! They ran to the lilac bush and squatted there laughing.

Soon, they heard Alice's mother again: 'Alice! Alice! Come here!'

Alice rushed to put on her shoes – but they were gone again, of course. They weren't behind that stone at all. Alice was in a dreadful rage. Once again she had to go to her mother with no shoes on her feet.

'Alice! You really are a very naughty little girl,' said her mother. 'That's another penny out of your money box, please. Well, you won't be able to buy that wheelbarrow if you go on like this.'

Alice ran down the garden, crying. That was a precious two pennies gone. She suddenly caught sight of her two shoes, sitting quietly behind the stone. She stared and stared. She could *not* understand how it was that they were there now, when she hadn't been able to find them a few minutes ago. It was really very puzzling.

Well, those shoes had a fine game with Alice that morning! Six times they ran off, and six times poor Alice had to go to her mother without her shoes on, and pay sixpence out of her money box. Now she wouldn't' be able to buy the wheelbarrow for ages!

There's something funny about those shoes, thought Alice to herself. *I shall just hide behind the summerhouse and watch them.*

So she did – and to her great surprise she saw them galloping off merrily to hide under the lilac bush. She ran after them, calling angrily, 'Shoes! Shoes! Where are you going? You've no right to hide away like that. You've got me into lots of trouble this morning.'

The shoes stopped and turned themselves round. '*We* didn't get you into trouble,' said the right shoe. 'You got yourself into it. If you'd put us on, everything would have been all right.'

'Well! I never knew shoes could talk before!' cried Alice in surprise.

'That shows how silly you are,' said the left shoe. 'You must know perfectly well, Alice, that lace-up shoes have tongues!'

'It's very unkind of you to disobey your mother,' said the left shoe. 'She only wants to save your feet from being cut or scratched. We're going to run away from you every time you take us off in the garden!'

'Then you'll have to give up all your money,' said the right shoe, with a little skip on the grass. 'And serve you right!'

'Well, you just *won't* run away any more!' said Alice angrily, and she took both the shoes into her hands. 'I shall put you on – and keep you on! And you won't be able to play horrid tricks on me any more!'

She put them both on and tied the laces tightly. The shoes grinned at one another.

'We've taught her a lesson,' whispered the right shoe to the left.

'She won't disobey again,' chuckled the left shoe, squeaking as Alice ran down the garden.

And she didn't! The next time her mother called her, she went at once – with both her shoes on! Her mother was pleased.

'At last you've decided to be a good girl,' she said to Alice. 'Just in time too, or you wouldn't have had a single coin left in your money box!'

I hope *your* shoes don't run off by themselves. Wouldn't you be surprised?

The Poppy Pixie

The Poppy Pixie

GRINNY WAS a jolly little pixie. He was very clever with his fingers, and made beautiful hats and caps from rose petals given to him by the rose fairy. He sewed them into pretty shapes with spider's thread and then sold them to the pixies.

But one day the rose fairy wouldn't let him have any more petals. She said she wanted them herself to make party frocks from. So Grinny had nothing to use for his hats and caps.

Now what shall I do? he thought. *If I don't work, I don't make money. And if I don't make money I can't buy food to eat. And if I don't have food I'll starve. So I must do something about it.*

He put on his hat and went for a walk beside the big golden cornfield that rustled softly in the breeze. Suddenly the wind came down, swept off his hat and threw it right on the top of an ear of corn! Grinny stared up at it. He couldn't get it at all. It was so far above his tiny head.

'Bother!' he said. 'There goes a perfectly good hat. Now what shall I do? The sun is so hot today that I shall certainly get sunstroke if I don't wear a hat.'

As he walked by a poppy that waved in the breeze, he saw below it two small green things. They had formed the green hat that the poppy had worn when it was still a bud.

Every poppy wears a green hat before it unfolds its red petals. Have you seen it? When the poppy is ready to shake out its silky flowers the green hat splits in two and falls to the ground. It is finished with! The poppy doesn't want it any more.

It was the green poppy hat, split in two halves, that

Grinny found. He picked up the halves. They had curled up a little and were nice and stiff.

'My goodness!' said Grinny. 'These are just the things for hats! With a little feather in they would be very smart indeed! Hey, Poppy! Do you want these green things?'

'No,' said the poppy, bending down its pretty red head. 'You can have them. I have thrown them away.'

Grinny picked them up and looked round for more. Beneath every poppy he found the little caps thrown away on the ground. He got as many as he could carry and then went home. How pleased he was! He fitted one on his cheeky little head, and it made a dear little long-shaped hat. He took it off and looked at it.

'If I make two holes in the side, I can fit the quill of a feather in, and the hat will look grand!' said Grinny. He looked about for something to make the holes. He found a little knife and cut the holes neatly. Then he went to where the long-tailed tit sat with her brood of tiny babies, and begged for a few feathers from her old nest. He knew that she used thousands of feathers to line it with.

She popped into the round nest and threw out about a hundred of the tiniest feathers she had collected there. Grinny was pleased.

He set to work to make the feathered hats. He made the holes in the poppy caps, stuck the feathers in, and there were the hats, all ready to sell!

He did sell them quickly too! The pixies and the elves were always ready to buy new hats, and these really did look smart. Even the snails came to buy one each, and Grinny chuckled away to himself when he saw the snails gliding away proudly, each with a poppy hat on its horns.

He made such a lot of money that he really felt he ought to share it with the poppies. So he went to tell them, and they listened, their pretty red heads swaying gently on their long stalks.

'We don't want any money,' they said. 'We don't need to buy anything. But, Grinny, we would be so glad if you would do something for us.'

'Anything I can!' said the little pixie.

'Well, listen,' said the poppies. 'When our red petals die and fall off, we are left with our little green seedheads. Inside are our precious seeds. Soon our green heads turn brown and hard and the seeds get ripe. They want to get out and find new homes, and sometimes they find it very difficult.'

'What can I do to help, then?' asked Grinny, puzzled.

'Could you make little windows in our seedheads with your tiny knife?' asked the poppies. 'Then, you see, our seeds could fly out of the windows every time the wind shakes our heads.'

'What a good idea!' said Grinny, pleased. 'Just tell me when you are ready and I'll come along and make the seed windows with my little knife. I'll make them just under the piece that sticks out at the top of your seedhead, then the rain won't get in.'

'Thank you!' said the poppies, and they danced in

the hot summer sun.

Each day Grinny went to see if the poppies were ready for him to make seed windows. Their red petals fell. Now only their green seedheads were left. They turned brown and hard.

'Now, Grinny!' they called to him one day. 'Bring your knife and make the holes for the windows. We are ready! Our seeds are black and ripe.'

So Grinny climbed up the green stalks and sat on the top of the poppyheads, one by one. He carved out tiny windows in the side, just under the top of the head, with his small knife. He really did them very well.

Then he slid down again. When the wind came and shook the poppyheads, the seeds flew right out of the windows Grinny had made, and fell to the ground, ready to grow into new poppy plants the next year.

The poppies were pleased. Grinny was pleased too. The poppies gave him caps to sell – and he gave them windows for their seeds to fly from. Good!

Would you like to see Grinny's little poppy windows? Well, find some ripe brown poppyheads and look for the windows. Shake the heads upside down and watch the seeds fly out like pepper from a pepper pot. Isn't it a good idea?

Mr Twiddle Cuts
the Grass

Mr Twiddle Cuts
the Grass

'I DO wish,' said Mrs Twiddle, 'I do wish, Twiddle, that you would do something about that long grass in the garden. It looks so very untidy.'

Mrs Twiddle said this almost every day. Mr Twiddle sighed. He knew he would have to cut that grass sooner or later. Well, it was a nice day. He might as well do it and get it over.

'Very well, my love,' he said. 'I'll take the scythe and cut it down. It's too long to mow. Anything to please you!'

'Well, put your garden trousers on, dear,' said Mrs Twiddle. 'You don't want to spoil your nice ones.'

Mr Twiddle went upstairs and found his garden trousers. They were old grey flannel ones and he liked them. They were big and comfortable.

He put them on and then took everything out of the pockets of his other trousers and put them into the pockets of his garden trousers. In went his money, his keys, his handkerchief and a little roll of string that he always kept in case he might want some.

Then he went downstairs to find the scythe. 'It may be blunt, of course,' he said to Mrs Twiddle. 'Then I couldn't start cutting the grass today.'

'Well, it isn't blunt,' said Mrs Twiddle. 'I had it sharpened last week for you. Now do get to work, Twiddle – you've been ages already getting your garden trousers on.'

Twiddle went out into the garden. It was rather hot. Oh dear, scything was very, very hard work! He would soon be dreadfully hot! He took off his coat.

He walked to the long grass with the big scythe in his hand. Dear, dear, it certainly was very long! He felt the blade of the scythe to see if it really was sharp, and it was.

Now, just as Mr Twiddle was about to begin his work, the cat walked over to him and rubbed against his leg in a very loving manner. Twiddle was not very fond of his wife's cat. It always wanted doors or windows opened for it whenever Twiddle was sitting down reading his paper.

'Go away, Puss!' he said, sternly. 'I'm going to do a bit of scything. You don't want your tail cut off, do you? Well, use your brains, then, and get away. Shoo!'

The cat rubbed itself against Mr Twiddle's other leg. Then it sat down and began to roll in the grass.

'Did you hear what I said?' asked Twiddle. 'Go away from this long grass. Right away. Surely you would not be silly enough to lie down and sleep in it just when I'm going to scythe it? Of course, I know that's just the kind of thing you would do!'

The cat immediately curled itself up in the grass

and tucked its head into its paws. Twiddle stirred it with his foot.

'Now, what did I say? Go and find Mrs Twiddle! Go along!'

The cat uncurled itself, went a little way away, gave Twiddle a nasty look and settled down again. Mr Twiddle began to get angry. He ran at the cat.

'Shoo! Get away! Why do you always make things difficult for me?'

The cat decided that Twiddle wanted to have a game with it. It jumped up, crouched down and ran at Twiddle's feet. Then it darted away into the grass and hid. Twiddle ran at it again. 'Shoo! Will you go away and let me get on with my work?'

Mrs Twiddle put her head out of the window. 'Twiddle! What are you doing rushing about in the grass all by yourself and shouting like that?'

'I'm not all by myself!' shouted back Twiddle, indignantly. 'The cat's here. How can I cut the grass if she's darting about the whole time?'

He chased the cat all about the grass and at last it ran off to Mrs Twiddle, its tail straight up in the air. Twiddle, feeling very hot, panted a bit, and then lifted the scythe.

But just as he was about to begin he saw something lying in the grass, something bright and round. He picked it up. A sixpence! Well, that was a nice little find. Very nice indeed. He put it into his pocket with his other money.

'It's a pity I can't find a bit more money,' he said to himself. 'If I could I'd pay a man to do this heavy scything.'

He cut a piece of grass, and then he suddenly saw something shining once more. He bent down – goodness gracious, it was a shilling!

'Very strange!' said Mr Twiddle. 'Someone's been walking in the grass, I suppose, and dropped a bit of money. Who's been trespassing in my garden? Well, it serves him right to lose his money!'

He lifted his scythe again, and then thought that he

might as well have a look to see if there was any more money lying in the long grass. So he put down his scythe and began to look.

He soon saw a penny and a ha'penny! Then he found another sixpence. Well, well, this was a nice surprise, to be sure! 'Two shillings and a penny ha'penny altogether. Splendid!'

He began to look very carefully indeed, bending down and peering in the grass, parting the long blades hopefully.

'Another shilling! Well, I never! And here's half-a-crown. Would you believe it! Why, this bit of grass is full of money!'

It was most extraordinary. He kept on picking up pennies and ha'pennies, sixpences and shillings, wherever he looked. He put them all into his pocket, feeling very pleased indeed. 'I shall get a man to come and do the scything now. Why, I must have picked up about a pound's worth of money already. Very nice, very nice indeed!'

Mrs Twiddle looked out of the window again to see if Twiddle was getting on well with his scything. She saw him bending down, creeping here and there, then suddenly standing up to put something into his pocket, then bending down again and creeping about. What was he doing?

'Twiddle!' shouted Mrs Twiddle. 'What do you think you're doing? Surely you're not playing with the cat?'

'I am not!' said Twiddle, standing up, looking rather hot. 'I'm picking up money.'

'Good gracious!' said Mrs Twiddle. 'Money! Whatever do you mean?'

'What I say,' said Twiddle, and bent down to pick up a sixpence. He held it up to show her. 'It's easy. I just look for it and I see it. It's all over this piece of grass. Wherever I go I find pennies and ha'pennies and sixpences and shillings and half-crowns. Why, here's half-a-crown by my foot now!'

So there was. Mrs Twiddle hurried down to the

patch of long grass. 'Really, Twiddle! I can't believe it. How could there be so much money in this grass? Where in the world did it come from?'

'Somebody must have dropped it,' said Twiddle. 'Somebody trespassing in my garden. Serves him right to lose it.'

He picked up sixpence and put it into his pocket. 'I'm going to pay a man to do this scything instead of me,' he said. 'And if you'd like to buy yourself a box of chocolates, I'd be pleased to give you the money. And we might perhaps buy a chicken for our dinner.'

Mrs Twiddle looked very puzzled. She couldn't understand this money business at all. Twiddle wandered away a little and then picked up a penny. 'See! I tell you wherever I go in this grass I pick up money.'

'Your pocket must be absolutely full of it!' said Mrs Twiddle. 'How much have you got?'

'Well, I've picked up dozens and dozens of pennies and sixpences and shillings and things,' said Twiddle.

'I'll show you what I've got.'

His put his hand into his pocket to get out all the money he had put there. He felt round his pocket and a frown came on his face.

'What's the matter?' said Mrs Twiddle.

'A most extraordinary thing,' said Twiddle, looking astonished. 'I can't feel even a *penny* in my pocket! And yet I put dozens of coins there. Where have they all gone?'

'Let me see,' said Mrs Twiddle, and she put her hand into his pocket and found a big hole at the bottom.

'Twiddle! You've got an enormous hole in that pocket. I really do think you are the stupidest man I've ever known! Here you go walking about with a hole in your pocket, dropping all your money out, and picking it up and putting it in your pocket again, then out it falls, and you pick it up all over again – and think you're so rich we can have chicken for dinner!'

Mr Twiddle stared at his wife in dismay. He felt the hole in his pocket. 'Have I – have I been picking up the same penny and the same sixpence and the same shilling all the time?' he said. 'Wasn't this grass full of money, then?'

'No, you stupid man! Whatever money was here fell from your pocket – when you were chasing the cat about, I should think,' said Mrs Twiddle. 'And you kept on picking it up and losing it and picking it up – oh, Twiddle, I think my cat's got more sense in its head than you have. Wasting all the morning doing a silly thing like that!'

Twiddle was very upset. He picked up a shilling by his foot and absent-mindedly put it into his pocket. It at once fell out and appeared by his foot again.

'See! That's what's been happening all the time,' said Mrs Twiddle. 'Now, you listen to me, Twiddle – I shan't give you any dinner at all till you've finished cutting this grass. So, if you want to play with the cat or go on picking up your money, you know what to expect!'

And little Mrs Twiddle walked back to the house

quite crossly. Twiddle sighed loudly, took his scythe and set to work.

What a disappointment – and how cross Mrs Twiddle looked. Then a thought came into Mr Twiddle's head. He threw down his scythe and ran across the garden till he came to the kitchen window. He popped his head in and made Mrs Twiddle jump.

'Now, you listen to me,' said Twiddle, quite fiercely. 'Do you know whose fault all this is? Yours, yours! And do you know why? Because you didn't mend the hole in my pocket! Aha! Aha!'

Then, feeling quite pleased with himself, Twiddle went happily back to the grass and scythed hard till it was all cut. And you will be glad to know that Mrs Twiddle had a lovely dinner ready for him, and gave him a hearty kiss when he came in.

'You're a dear old thing, even if you are stupid!' she said. 'Now, don't you dare to say "Aha!" to me again, or I shall laugh till I cry. Aha, indeed!'

The Two Poor Children

The Two Poor
Children

THERE WERE once two poor children who lived by the seaside. Their mother had so little money to spare that she was always glad when the summer came because then they did not need many clothes to wear.

Their names were George and Mollie. They loved the sands and the sea, and every day in the summer holidays they went to play on the shore.

They were well-behaved children, with good manners, and the other children liked them.

'Come and help dig a castle, George!' shouted Billy.

But George and Mollie had no spades. They only had two old buckets, one without a handle, that they had found thrown away on the beach. So they couldn't help to dig castles.

'We're having a sailing match on the big pool today,' said Jenny to Mollie the next day. 'Bring your boats and we'll all sail them together.'

But George and Mollie had no boats. They couldn't bathe because they had no swimsuits. They couldn't go shrimping because they had no nets. They could only paddle, or play ball with the other children when they brought out their balls.

One day George trod on some broken glass on the beach and cut his foot a little, for neither he nor Mollie had shoes for the sands. Their mother had no money to spare for special beach shoes, and as they were not allowed to wear their ordinary shoes on the sand in case they got spoilt, the children went barefoot.

'Look at all this glass!' said George. 'It's so dangerous to leave it about! Most of the other children have shoes, lucky things – but some of them like to leave them off when their mothers are not looking.'

'We'd better pick up the glass then, in case they get their feet cut like yours,' said Mollie. 'We can use our buckets.'

So every day after that the two children hunted for broken glass and put all the bits they found into their buckets. They emptied the glass into the litter bins.

'Why do you bother to pick up that broken glass?' asked Billy one day. 'You might cut your fingers.'

'We are very careful not to,' said George. 'We're picking it up so that none of you will cut your feet. You only come down here for two or three weeks, Billy, and if you cut your feet and can't walk for some time you'll miss half your holiday! We live here, so it's not so bad for us – but we wouldn't like to see any of you with cut feet. You are always so nice to us.'

'Come and shrimp with us this afternoon,' said Billy.

'We can't,' said Mollie. 'We haven't got nets. Look, Billy, how full of glass our buckets are today! Somebody must have been setting up bottles and throwing stones at them. That's a really wicked thing to do!'

Billy's mother saw the two poor children emptying their buckets into the litter bin again, and she asked Billy about them.

When she heard that they always picked up the glass so that it should not cut the children's feet on holiday, Billy's mother looked at her little boy.

'George and Mollie have no spades,' she said. 'They have no nets, and no swimming costumes. They only have those old broken buckets – and they use them so that you, Billy, and the other children, will not cut their feet! I think you should do something for them, as they do something for you.'

'Oh, Mother! That's a good idea!' said Billy. 'We all like George and Mollie, and it's a pity when they can't go swimming and shrimping and digging with us. I'll go and tell the other children, and we'll see what we can do for them.'

He ran off. The other children gathered round him

and heard what he had to say. They were delighted to think they could help the two children.

'Let's look in our money boxes and see what we've got,' said Lucy.

So they did. Lucy had ninepence. Billy had one and threepence. Jane had twopence. Allan had sixpence. Mary had two whole shillings. John had two halfpennies. Jenny had five pennies and a farthing.

They all brought their money to Billy's mother that afternoon. She put some of her own to it, and then took the children shopping in the town.

They bought two large wooden spades. They bought two new buckets, one red and one green. They bought two blue swimming costumes and two pairs of beach shoes. They bought a fishing net for George and a ball for Mollie. Goodness, how pleased all the children were when they got back to the beach! It is such fun to give a surprise to somebody who isn't expecting it.

'Mollie! George!' called Billy. 'Come here! You are

always picking up glass for us so that we shan't cut our feet. Now we want to do something for you!'

The children gave George and Mollie all the things they had bought. The two children stared at all the things in joy and wonder. They had never had so many presents in their lives!

'Oh, thank you!' they cried. 'It is nice of you! Now we shall be able to do everything you do!'

They put on their little swimsuits. They took up their spades and new buckets – they were ready for anything! And now George and Mollie can dig and swim and shrimp and fish whenever the others do.

But they still do their little job of picking up the broken glass. They never forget that, whatever happens! Isn't that nice of them?

Pretty-Star the Pony

Pretty-Star the Pony

I AM a little black pony, and my name is Pretty-Star because I have a pretty white star right in the middle of my forehead.

I used to live in Farmer White's field, and eat the sweet grass there. I didn't like Farmer White, for he was a rough man with a loud voice that made me jump with fright. When he rode me I felt as if my back was going to give way, for he was so heavy. He gave me the whip, too, and that is enough to break any willing pony's heart, for I never needed it.

A little girl called Mary used to come and see me every day. She lived in a house near to Farmer White's and went to school on her bicycle every morning. On her way there and back she would stop and speak to me. Sometimes she brought me lumps of sugar, or an apple.

'I wish you were *my* pony,' she would say. 'I would love to have you for my very own. I would ride you to school every day, and look after you well, dear little Pretty-Star. When my birthday comes I am going to ask my daddy to buy you for me.'

One day her bicycle had a puncture, so she came and asked Farmer White if he would lend me to her to ride to school on. He said yes, so she put my saddle and bridle on, and jumped up on my back. How proud I was to carry her! I neighed gladly, and trotted along carefully. She was as light as a feather, and didn't pull at my mouth a bit. She talked to me all the way, and though I couldn't answer her in her own language, I loved to hear her voice.

She gave me an apple and tied me up to the school gate in the shade of a tree, just within reach of some nice juicy grass. There I waited patiently until she came out to go home again.

'Oh, Pretty-Star, I *wish* you were my very own pony,' she said, when she let me loose in Farmer White's field again. 'I am sure we should love each other dearly.'

When her birthday came she brought her father to see me.

'Daddy, will you give me this little black pony for my birthday?' she asked. 'I want him more than anything else in the world.'

'But what would you do with him?' asked her father. 'You've got your bicycle to ride to school on. You'd soon get tired of having to look after a real live pony. It's not like a bicycle, you know, Mary. You couldn't just put him in a shed and leave him there till you wanted him. He would have to be fed, and groomed carefully.'

'Yes, Daddy,' said Mary. 'I know just how to groom him, and I could take care of him much better than

Farmer White does, really I could. He doesn't care a bit for him.'

I nuzzled my nose into Mary's hand, and looked at her father pleadingly, for I wanted to belong to Mary. But the big man shook his head.

'No,' he said. 'I must disappoint you, Mary. The pony is quite a nice little thing, but he is not worth the price Farmer White is asking. I'll buy you a big doll instead.'

Mary didn't say any more, but she gave me a hug and a kiss, and I knew better than her father how sad she was not to have me for her own.

Mary got her big doll, but she wouldn't play with it. She was the sort of person who likes real live pets that love her back when she loves them. She came to see me every day, and I whinnied a welcome, and ran to meet her.

One day she came to the nearby river to fish with her big boy cousin. I stood as near to them as I could, but I couldn't get very near because of a high hedge in between. Mary waved to me when she saw my head over the hedge, and I whinnied back.

I watched them all the morning. They didn't catch any fish, and the big boy was impatient.

'Let's climb up on this rock where there's a deep, quiet pool beneath,' he said. 'I'm sure there are plenty of fish there, Mary.'

'We must be careful then,' said Mary. 'It is dangerous to climb up there, my daddy says.'

I knew it was, too, and I watched them anxiously. They had just reached the top of the rock when Mary slipped. She clutched at the boy and missed him. Then she fell right over the rock and I heard her fall – splash! – into the deep pool below.

'Mary, Mary!' called the boy. 'Can you swim?'

I knew she wasn't able to, but of course I couldn't tell him that. I was so anxious that I didn't know what to do. I couldn't get out of my field, for the gate was shut, and I ran whinnying round and round and round, thinking of Mary in the water. I hoped the boy would dive in and rescue her, but he didn't.

I suddenly saw him start running off towards the house where Mary lived. He was calling 'Help! Help! Mary is in the water!' as he ran.

Well, I knew that the little girl would drown if no one rescued her soon, and I was almost mad with grief. I decided to get to the river if I only could. So I ran backwards a few paces, then galloped full tilt at the high hedge. Over I went, with my hooves just touching the top. I have never jumped so high before, and I don't suppose I ever shall again.

Once over the hedge I raced down to the river. I looked into the water, and soon saw where Mary was. She was holding on to a broken bough of a tree that dipped down to the river, and I knew that it would soon break off altogether, and then my little friend would drown.

I jumped straight into the river myself, and began to swim towards Mary. I had nearly got to her when the bough broke right off, and the little girl went under the water. She came up spluttering and gasping – but she saw me.

'Help me, Pretty-Star!' she cried – then down she went again.

In a trice I was up to her. I plucked hold of her wet clothes with my strong teeth, and pulled her up. She came up spluttering again, and caught hold of my neck.

'Hold on tightly,' I said in my horse language that she understood so well. So she held on whilst I turned myself carefully round in the water, and began to swim for the shallow bank. The current was against me, and it was very difficult. I am only a little pony, and Mary seemed very heavy, with all her wet clothes dragging her down. I began to gasp and pant myself, and I felt as if my heart was bursting in two.

Then I saw some people running towards the river. There was the boy and Mary's father and mother, and the gardener, too, carrying a rope. They all ran to the bank, and looked down on Mary and me.

'The pony's got her! He must have jumped right over the hedge!' cried Mary's father in amazement.

'Oh, the brave little pony!' cried Mary's mother, with tears streaming down her cheeks.

Just at that moment I reached the bank, and stumbled out of the water. I was so exhausted that I had to lie down in the mud. Mary's father picked her up and cuddled her, and her mother cried tears all over her.

'I'm all right, Daddy,' said Mary. 'But just look at that poor little tired pony. I'm sure he must nearly have burst his heart in two, swimming against the river like that.'

Fancy her knowing that! That just shows how she loved me. Of course, I soon felt better, then, dear me, the petting I had! It was wonderful!

Nobody could make enough of me. I had sugar and apples, and everyone stroked my nose and patted me. It was lovely.

But the nicest reward of all was still to come.

'Mary, we'll take the pony back to Farmer White now,' said her father. 'And if he's still willing to sell him, you shall have him. He deserves to belong to you, for I never saw such a plucky little creature in my life!'

Farmer White said he was quite willing to sell me. So Mary's father paid for me that same day, and Mary rode on my back to her home. I was her very own pony at last!

And now I am as happy as the day is long, for I take Mary to and from school every day, and we always go for a long ride together in the evenings. On Saturdays we go out all day long together, and on Sundays I take her to church. Don't you think I am a very lucky little pony?

The Tin Whistle

The Tin Whistle

PAUL HAD a tin whistle that had a very loud whistle indeed. His mother got very tired of it. 'Paul! If you don't stop blowing that whistle I shall take it away and put it into the dustbin!' she cried.

'Oh no, Mother!' said Paul in alarm. 'It's the best one I've ever had.'

'Well, go into the woods and play there,' said Mother. 'You can whistle all you like there, for there is no one to hear you! Maybe the birds will get a bit tired of you, but they can always fly away, and I can't!'

So Paul went to the woods with his tin whistle. He blew it and he blew it, and at last he had no breath left.

'I'll climb a tree and have a rest,' he said. 'It shall be my ship, swaying on the sea.'

So he climbed a big tree and sat near the top, swaying in the wind, for all the world like a ship bobbing to and fro on the sea.

After a while he got out his tin whistle and looked at it. 'I think I shall be the guard of a train now,' he said. 'The tree is the train. When I blow my whistle the train must go!'

But before he blew his whistle again, he heard voices. They were the voices of two boys. Paul peeped down to the bottom of the tree. The boys were standing underneath, talking.

'Now, I'll creep through the hedge into Farmer Brown's strawberry field with my basket,' said one boy, 'and you stay here and keep watch for me. You can see the road well from here. If you see anyone coming, whistle. See? Then I shall hear your whistle and come back before I'm caught. We'll share whatever strawberries I get.'

Ooh, the naughty bad boys! thought Paul, shocked. *Those are my daddy's strawberries. Those boys mean to steal them! What shall I do? If I climb down and tell them to go away, they will fight me and knock me down. But I can't stay here and see Daddy's fruit stolen!*

The first boy was already creeping through the hedge with his basket. The other boy was standing beneath the tree, watching the road, which could be seen clearly from where he stood.

Then Paul had a marvellous idea. He put his tin whistle to his mouth and blew hard. *Pheeeeeeeee!*

The boy who was climbing through the hedge at once squeezed back again, and ran to join his friend in the wood.

'Is there somebody coming?' he asked. 'I heard your whistle.'

'Well, I didn't whistle,' said the other boy, puzzled.

'You must have!' said the first boy. 'I heard you!'

'Well *I* heard a whistle too, but it wasn't *me* whistling,' said his friend. 'Go on – try again. No one's coming.'

Paul let the boy get right into the field, then he blew on his whistle again: *Pheeeeeeeee! Pheeeeeeeee!* At once the boy scrambled back through the hedge and ran helter-skelter into the wood. 'You whistled again!' he panted. 'Who's coming?'

'Nobody. And I didn't whistle, and I can't think who did!' said the second boy angrily, looking all round. 'Perhaps it was a bird.'

'It *was* you whistling!' said the other boy. 'I know your whistle. You are just playing tricks on me.'

'No, I'm not,' said the second boy. 'Go on – try again.'

But as soon as the boy got into the field, Paul whistled even more loudly than before: PHEEEEEE-EEE! PHEEEEEEEEE! PHEEEEEEEEE!

Back came the boy, panting. 'That *was* your whistle!' he cried. 'Is there anyone coming?'

'No, there isn't, and it *wasn't* my whistle I tell you,' said the boy, half afraid, looking all round him.

'Whoever can be whistling here?'

Then Paul thought he would try a big deep voice and see what would happen. So he said in a growly, fierce voice, 'BAD BOYS! WICKED BOYS! I CAN SEE YOU! WAIT TILL I CATCH YOU!'

'Oh! Oh! It's the farmer!' cried the boys, and they ran off through the wood at top speed, leaving their basket behind them. Paul blew a long blast on his whistle and climbed down the tree. He picked up the basket and went home to tell his mother what had happened, blowing his whistle hard all the time.

'Paul! Stop!' cried his mother. 'That dreadful whistle!'

'Well, just listen what it did!' said Paul proudly, and he told his mother how the whistle had saved his father's strawberries. How his mother laughed! She was very pleased.

'That was clever of you, Paul,' she said. 'Well, well! As it's such a smart whistle I suppose I'll have to let you blow it as much as you like. Blow away!'

'No, I won't annoy you, Mother!' said Paul. 'I'll only blow it loudly in the woods. And maybe it will scare some more strawberry thieves away. I shouldn't be at all surprised.'

And neither should I!

The Dog Who Would Go Digging

The Dog Who Would Go Digging

PETE BELONGED to Dickie and Joan. He was the jolliest pup in the world, and there was nothing he liked better than having a game with you. He would let you try to catch him, if you liked the game of 'It'. He would rush miles after a ball if you wanted to play 'Ball', and if you just wanted to go for a walk, why, he'd go with you all the way there and back.

So you can guess that the children loved him very much. Mummy thought he was a nice little dog too – and so did Daddy, until one day he caught Pete digging in the garden!

'Hey, you rascal! Come off the beds!' yelled Daddy.

'How dare you! You're spoiling all the seeds I planted.'

Pete stopped – but as soon as Daddy's back was turned, he was digging again!

You see, he had suddenly discovered that it was good fun to bury the bones he couldn't eat! Then when he felt hungry he could dig them up and gnaw them. But, of course, as he hadn't a very good memory he couldn't always remember where he had buried his bones – so he had to dig here and dig there until at last he found them.

Daddy didn't like him digging here and digging there, for Daddy did the garden. It was Daddy who planted the seeds, and the bulbs, Daddy who carefully planted the little pansy plants, and forget-me-nots and the wallflowers. Daddy loved the garden and spent all his spare time there. So no wonder he was cross when Pete dug everything up!

Then there came a dreadful week, when Pete dug up the garden *every* day! Yes – he dug up the candytuft seeds; he dug up three nice pansy plants;

he dug up all the poppy seedlings that had come up so nicely in one big patch. And worst of all he took it into his silly little head that he had buried a bone underneath Daddy's best rose tree! So he even dug up the rose tree!

Daddy got crosser and crosser – and at last he said a dreadful thing.

'Pete must go. I'm not going to spend all my spare time working to make the garden nice, only to have Pete digging it all up every five minutes. If you children can't teach him to be good, I shall give him to the milkman. He wants a dog, I know.'

Oh my goodness! You should have seen poor Joan and Dickie! They went quite pale with fright. How *could* Daddy think of giving their own puppy away to the milkman? Why, they loved him with all their hearts – he was the nicest puppy in the world. They simply couldn't do without him.

'Please, Daddy, don't do that,' said Joan, her eyes full of tears. 'He doesn't mean to dig up your seeds.'

'I don't care if he means to or not,' said Daddy crossly. 'He does it just the same. Anyway, he goes to the milkman next week if he does any more damage.'

Well, Joan and Dickie did their best to make Pete behave – but one evening when they had gone out to play with a friend, Pete dug an enormous hole in the middle of Daddy's row of garden peas, which were *just* coming up.

'Give him to the milkman on Monday,' he said. 'I'm tired of him, and I'm not going to waste my time doing things that Pete simply undoes the very next minute.'

The children knew it was no good saying anything. When Daddy spoke like that he meant what he said. But how unhappy they were! How wet their pillows were that night! They did so love Pete – he really was such a dear, fat, playful fellow. If only he wouldn't dig up poor Daddy's garden! But it was no use – he had done it once too often and now he must go away.

Sunday came. Daddy took Mummy and the two children out for a bus ride to see the buttercup fields, which were just like golden carpets then. Pete was left behind. And, of course, in his little doggy mind he thought, *Ha! A good time for digging! Now where's that bone I buried two days ago?*

He ran into the garden. He found a nice corner under a big old lilac bush, and then began to dig. How he dug! He felt sure the bone was there. He was going to dig until he found it, anyway, even if he dug a hole as big as a house.

Scrape, scrape, scrape, went his strong little paws. Snuffle, snuffle, snuffle, went his nose! Ah! Here was the bone at last! Scrape, scrape, scrape!

What a large bone! Pete didn't remember that it was so large when he had buried it. Goodness, it must have grown since he buried it. Well, things grew in the ground – seeds shot up – plants grew – perhaps bones grew as well. Ha, what a fine bone it would be!

Pete panted and puffed, scraped and snuffled – but he couldn't get that bone up. It was too big and too heavy. So he sat down for a rest, his tongue hanging out. And there Daddy and the children found him, when they got home.

'That dog has been digging again!' cried Daddy in a rage. He ran up to the lilac bush, and Pete shot away. Daddy looked into the hole, and then he looked again.

'Is it one of Pete's bones?' asked Joan, sorry that the puppy should have behaved badly again. 'Oh Daddy! It's not a bone! It's a funny old box! Look, Pete has got one end out – but it was too big for him to get right out! I expect he thought it was a very big bone!'

'Whatever is it?' asked Dickie, excitedly. 'Quick, Daddy, get it up!'

Daddy was red with excitement too. Whatever could the box be? He fetched his spade and began to dig it up. At last he and Dickie lifted it up on to the grass – and then Joan cried out in surprise.

'Oh! It's got our name on it – look – it says

'PAGET'. That's our name, isn't it, Daddy? You're Mr Paget and Mummy's Mrs Paget. Why is it on this old box?'

'My dears,' said Daddy, still red with excitement, 'my dears, I *believe* it must the box of jewels belonging to your great-grandmother, who lived in this same house. They were stolen by a burglar and never found again. He must have buried them in the garden, and then never had the chance to get them again.'

Well, Daddy was right! You should have seen the lovely things in that box! Great-Grandma had been a beauty and had had wonderful necklaces, bracelets and brooches. Some Daddy said he would keep for Mummy and Joan – others he would sell, and they would bring a lot of money.

How the children clapped their hands! How Mummy cried out for joy to see the pretty things! What excitement to find treasure like that, hidden for so many years!

Nobody thought of Pete, who had found it quite by mistake.

Pete heard the excitement and he longed to join in. He put his little nose round the door and said 'Wuff!' in a small, quiet voice, in case Daddy was still angry with him.

But Daddy wasn't. Dear me no! Pete had really done some good with his digging this time, so there was no scolding for him, only petting and lots of biscuits.

'You won't give him to the milkman now, will you, Daddy?' asked Joan, hugging the puppy tightly.

'No,' said Daddy. 'He's not a bad little chap. And besides, if he digs up the garden any more we shall be able to afford a gardener to put the damage right, with all the money that will come from these jewels!'

'WUFF WUFF!' barked Pete, joyfully. And wasn't it a very funny thing – he never in his life dug in the garden again! Joan said he must have been digging for the treasure all the time, and so of course, stopped digging when he found it. Mummy says he must have had enough of digging, and decided to be a grown-up dog. What do *you* think?

Rufus Pays Back

Rufus Pays Back

JEAN AND Donald were always busy in the garden. Their father had no gardener, and as he was working all day long, he never had much time for the garden, except in the late evening when he was tired.

So Jean and Donald did all they could to help. They were really very good little gardeners. I will tell you some of the things they did.

Well, every fortnight they sowed a long row of lettuce seed, not too thickly. Then, when the tiny green lettuces came up, they thinned them carefully.

'If we don't thin them properly, the lettuces will be too close together when they are big, Jeanie,' said

Donald, 'then they won't make nice hearts – and I do love eating the heart of a lettuce, don't you?'

Then they hoed and weeded the garden well. Jean was very good at weeding. She knew how to use the hoe, too, and you should have seen her hoeing away at the tiny weeds showing their green heads above the earth!

'If I can hoe them up when they are small like this,' she said to Donald, 'they won't be any trouble at all! It's when weeds grow big and make seeds that fly all over the garden that they are really a nuisance.'

Another thing they did was to stick the peas for Mother. As soon as the new-sown peas showed through the ground Donald fetched sticks, and the two children carefully set a double row of sticks down the peas, so that the tiny, curling tendrils could catch hold of the sticks and pull the pea plants high into the air.

So you see they were very useful children, and their mother and father were proud of them.

One day, when Jean and Donald were busy hoeing and weeding, they heard a rich little song nearby. They looked up and saw a small robin redbreast, his large black eyes looking at them.

'Look! Look at that dear little robin,' said Jean. 'Oh, Donald – I do hope he gets tame. Don't let's frighten him at all.'

The robin flew down almost to their feet, picked up a grub and flew back to his perch. He swallowed the grub, cocked his head on one side and sang a little song again, very short and sweet.

After that he followed the children about the garden whenever they appeared. He pecked up any worm or grub or caterpillar they dug up, and fed very well indeed. He became plump, and his red breast feathers shone and glowed.

'We'll call him Rufus,' said Donald. 'That means red. He's so very, very red, isn't he!'

So they called him Rufus, and soon he was so tame that he would perch on the handle of their spade or fork, if they left it standing anywhere, or on the handle of their watering can. He really was very sweet and the children loved him.

'I hope the next-door cat never gets him,' said Jean anxiously. 'She's such a clever cat at catching birds.'

But Rufus was very sharp. As soon as he saw the big black cat jumping over the fence, he flew to the top of the lilac tree and warned all the other birds by making a curious ticking sound.

'Tick-tick-tick-tick,' he said. 'Tick-tick-tick-tick!'

Then all the birds would hear and be on the lookout. 'He makes a noise like Daddy's fishing rod line being unreeled!' said Donald. 'Tick-tick-tick-tick-tick. Do you hear it?'

The children grew used to Rufus and his song and ticking noises. When they heard him singing they would whistle back cheerfully, and Jean would call out to him.

'Hallo, Rufus! Are you waiting for us? We're coming to garden now.'

Then the little robin would fly down and wait about for the first grub.

Whenever they heard him 'ticking' the children would look round to see what was the matter – and one day he ticked and ticked! It was very, very hot, and the children wore only their sunsuits. They worked in the garden, and all the time they heard the 'tick-tick-tick' of the robin.

They could see no cat in the garden, and certainly there was no dog. What could be the matter?

Jean went in to tell Mother. 'There's something the matter with Rufus,' she said. 'He keeps making that ticking noise. He's upset about something.'

'I expect he feels hot, just as you do, and doesn't like it,' said Mother. 'Look – here is a shallow earthenware dish – take it out and fill it with water from the garden tap. Then put it down for Rufus to drink from and bathe in. After all, there is no stream near here, and no pond. I daresay he is very thirsty.'

'Oh, I didn't think of that,' said Jean, and she took

the dish her mother gave her. She and Donald filled it under the garden tap, and then they put it down on the grass.

With a joyful, creamy song the robin flew down to it at once. He sipped water from it, tilting back his head, and letting it trickle down his throat.

'I always think it looks such a nice way to drink,' said Donald. 'Just take a little water in your mouth, then hold your head back and let it run down your throat. Oh, I say – what's Rufus going to do now?'

Rufus was paddling in the dish. The water was shallow, just up to the middle of his long legs. He suddenly put down his head, flicked out his wings and scattered drops of water all over himself!

'He's bathing! Oh, isn't he sweet!' said Donald. 'Mother, come and look – Rufus has had a drink and now he is bathing!'

Rufus bathed about twenty times a day. Other birds came to bathe and drink too. Rufus chased them away if he was there. He seemed to know that Jean and

Donald had really put out the bowl for him. 'But you mustn't be selfish, Rufus,' said Jean, seriously. 'You must let the others have a turn, too!'

The children went on with their gardening week after week. They sowed some lettuces. They watered the tomatoes in the greenhouse and watched one or two beginning to turn red. They watered the big marrow plants, and loved to see the marrows forming. Really, gardening was great fun.

But it had its tiresome times, too – and one of them was when the green caterpillars began to eat the new cabbages! Jean noticed one day that a good many of the cabbage leaves were full of holes. She went to see why – and then she called Donald.

'Donald! *Look* at our cabbages! Just look! There are big green caterpillars in almost every one!'

'Gracious!' said Donald. 'How dreadful! Look at *this* cabbage – the heart is eaten almost away. Oh, Jeanie – we shall have to pick out all these horrid caterpillars and kill them.'

It was a most unpleasant job. Jeanie hated it. She hated putting her hand into the heart-leaves of the big cabbages and trying to get hold of a soft, squirming caterpillar. She said it made her feel ill.

'I say! I wish Rufus would come and help!' said Donald at last. 'Where is he?'

'Having a bath,' said Jeanie, looking at the bowl on the lawn. 'Oh – I know! Let's put his bowl here, in the middle of the cabbages! Then perhaps he will think to himself, "Now why have they moved my bowl?" And he will guess we want his help with the caterpillars!'

So Donald carried the bowl to the cabbages, and set it down in the middle of them, where there was a little space. Rufus flew from bush to bush, following him in surprise. Why was Donald taking the bath away?

'Now listen, Rufus,' said Donald, solemnly. 'Here's your chance to pay us back for making a pet of you! See these cabbages – and see this caterpillar I'm taking out of this one – well, we want your help with them, please!'

Rufus saw the fat green caterpillar, flew down to Donald's hand and took it in his beak. He flew back to his bush, and in a second the caterpillar was gone!

'Did you see that?' said Donald, pleased. 'Isn't he awfully tame now?'

The children went to work nearby, clipping the edges of the grass. They watched Rufus out of the corners of their eyes. He flew down to his bowl to make quite sure it *was* his. He had a bath in it and flicked the water all over the cabbages. Then he sang a little song. Then he flew to a cabbage and sat on the top of it. His quick black eye caught sight of something moving in it, and he darted into the heart of the leaves at once. One quick peck and he was up again – with a giant green caterpillar in his beak.

'Oh, *good*!' said Jean, pleased. 'He knows what we want him to do, Donald! Isn't he good? He's really paying us back for our kindness to him.'

Rufus worked hard that morning. He visited every cabbage, stood on top of it, looked into the heart, and then if there was a caterpillar there he would find it and gobble it up.

'Mother, Rufus is a marvellous help to us,' said Donald. 'He's eaten about twenty caterpillars!'

Rufus was full up. He didn't seem to want any more to eat all that day, not even a wireworm that Donald offered him. He flew to a bough, and watched the children working. But next day he was hard at work on the cabbages again!

'He must have found about *thirty* caterpillars today!' said Jean. 'He's getting fatter and fatter! Look how he sticks his little red chest out! Let's have a look at the cabbages, shall we? They won't be eaten nearly so much now.'

They weren't. The new leaves that grew in the hearts of the cabbages were fresh and uneaten. The hearts were firm and solid. Rufus was proud of himself. Not one caterpillar would he leave in those cabbages.

Impy Plays a Trick

Impy Plays a Trick

IMPY LIVED next door to Mister Frown. He was afraid of Mister Frown, who looked as cross as his name. Mister Frown had no time for imps. He thought they were a tiresome nuisance, and he said so, very loudly, whenever he saw Impy in the distance.

'Nasty little nuisances!' he said. 'They never do any work. They are lazy, good-for-nothing creatures. Wait till I get hold of one!'

So, as you can guess, Impy kept well out of Mister Frown's way. The worst of it was that when Impy played with his ball in his garden, it would bounce over into Mister Frown's garden! And his kite would fly down there! And his arrows would dart straight into Mister Frown's garden and stay there.

Impy didn't dare to go and get them. He didn't even dare to ask for them. He just peeped over the wall very sadly, and saw all his nice toys next door. He knew Mister Frown would never throw them back to him.

Mister Frown saw them there and he grinned to himself.

'Ho!' he said. 'So that tiresome little Impy has lost some of his toys! Well, let him! I'm not going to throw them back – he can go without them. He won't dare to ask me for them.'

But one day something else of Impy's went into Mister Frown's garden. Impy had done his washing, and had washed his best yellow coat, his new yellow scarf and his yellow stockings. He had pegged them up on the line, and there they waved in the wind.

But Impy's pegs were not very good. They were old, and that day the wind blew very strongly indeed.

You should have seen how those clothes pulled at the pegs! And it wasn't very long before the wind pulled the clothes right off the line and into Mister Frown's garden next door.

Impy was looking out of his window when it happened. He went quite pale when he saw what was happening. First his coat went – then the stockings and then the lovely yellow scarf! They all flapped quickly over the wall, and draped themselves neatly on the rosebushes next door.

'Look at that!' said Impy to himself. 'Now what am I to do? All my balls are next door, and my fine red kite, and all my arrows belonging to my wooden box, and now my best clothes have blown there. Whatever shall I do?'

Should he go and ask for them? No – he dared not do that. Should he wait till Mister Frown was out? No – for he might come back and catch him. That would be dreadful!

Poor little Impy. He sat and thought for a long

while and then he grinned a little grin. He had thought of an idea but he didn't know if it would work or not.

He hunted for his long measuring tape. Then he set out to the market. He knew that Mister Frown would be along that way to do his shopping very soon. And Impy had a plan to keep him away long enough for him to get the things he had lost.

Impy hummed a little tune, undid his long measuring tape and pretended to measure the wall and the pavement near a corner of the street. Nobody took any notice of him. They thought he was a workman doing a job.

Presently along came Mister Frown, carrying his shopping bag. He was surprised to see Impy with his measuring tape.

'First time I've ever seen you working, Impy,' he said. 'Dear, dear, this is very strange!'

'I'm very busy,' said Impy. 'I've got to make notes about this corner of the street, and measure it carefully. The worst of it is that I've no one to hold the other end of the measure for me. So the tape keeps slipping.'

'Well, I don't mind holding it for you,' said Mister Frown, thinking that as long as Impy was at the other end of the tape he certainly couldn't slip home and take his clothes from the garden. 'I'll hold one end.'

'Oh, thank you, Mister Frown, how very kind you are!' said Impy. He held out one end of the tape to Mister Frown who took it.

'Now would you please hold it tightly while I pop round the corner with the other end of the tape?' asked Impy. 'Keep a good pull on it, won't you, so that we get the length quite right. I have to measure from here to right round the corner.'

Mister Frown held the end of the tape tightly. He saw Impy go round the corner. He felt someone at the other end, holding it tightly. He thought Impy was holding it just as tightly as he was.

But Impy wasn't! Impy had found Tickles the brownie round the corner and had beckoned to him.

'Here, Tickles! Would you be good enough to hold

the end of this tape for me while I go round the corner and hold the other end? I want to measure just here.'

Tickles took the other end at once. Impy thanked him, slipped across the road, went down a side turning, and ran home as fast as ever he could – leaving his measuring tape carefully held by Mister Frown and Tickles. They couldn't see one another because they were each round a corner – and, dear me, they each thought that the other end of the tape was held by Impy!

Impy giggled as he ran home. He rushed into Mister Frown's garden and quickly found his balls, his kite, his arrows and his clothes. He threw everything except his clothes over the wall, and then, carrying his yellow coat, stockings and scarf he slipped out of Mister Frown's garden and into his own house. He locked the door and shut the windows.

He waited for Mister Frown to come home. What would he say? What was he doing now?

Well, Mister Frown was not a very patient man,

and after he had held the tape for about four minutes he began to frown. Tickles, the brownie, thought that Impy was being a long time too, and he pulled impatiently on the tape.

Mister Frown felt the pull, and he pulled back.

'Hurry up!' yelled Mister Frown.

'Hurry up yourself!' Tickles yelled back.

Mister Frown tugged the tape crossly and Tickles almost fell over. He jerked his end roughly too, and Mister Frown fell over his shopping bag and hurt his knee.

'Stop it!' yelled Mister Frown angrily.

'Well, you stop it then!' shouted Tickles.

'I'll come and spank you!' roared Mister Frown, and letting go of his end of the tape he rushed round the corner, expecting to find Impy holding the other end. But to his great surprise he saw Tickles there!

'What are you holding that for?' he asked.

'Because Impy asked me to,' said Tickles.

Mister Frown stared in amazement. 'But he asked

me as well!' he said. 'I've been holding on all this time – and so have you too. Well, where is Impy?'

'I don't know,' said Tickles crossly. 'This is just one of his silly tricks, I suppose. Goodbye. I'm off!'

Mister Frown stared after him, thinking hard. A trick, was it? Ah – now he had it – Impy wanted to get home and take those clothes that had blown into the garden – and he had played this trick on Mister Frown so that he could keep him safely out of the way.

'*Grrr*!' Mister Frown growled like a dog and shot off down the street, quite forgetting his shopping bag. He ran all the way home, puffing and panting. As soon as he got into his back garden he saw that the balls, the kite, the arrows and the clothes had all gone!

'Oh, the artful imp! Oh, the sly fellow!' cried Mister Frown in a rage, and he ran up the path to Impy's door.

He banged hard. No answer. He knocked again. Still no answer.

He went to the windows. They were shut and

fastened. But when Mister Frown peeped into one, he saw Impy sitting indoors, dressed in his yellow clothes, grinning away for all he was worth.

'You played a trick on me, you wicked imp!' roared Mister Frown. 'How dare you make me hold that tape when all you wanted was to get back home and take things out of my garden!'

Just then Mister Plod the policeman came by, and when he heard what Mister Frown said he went up to him.

'What's all this?' he said. 'Has Impy been taking things out of your garden?'

'Yes,' said Mister Frown. 'He has.'

'That's stealing,' said Mister Plod. 'What has he taken?'

'Four balls, six arrows, one kite and a suit of yellow clothes!' yelled Impy, opening the window.

'You naughty little imp!' said the policeman. 'Who did they belong to?'

'They belonged to me!' said Impy with a grin.

'Well, you can't steal things from yourself,' said Mister Plod, shutting his notebook. 'Mister Frown, don't be silly. Go home and behave yourself.'

So Mister Frown went to his own house, red with rage – and Impy began to sing, 'Oh, dear, what can the matter be?' at the top of his naughty little voice.

A Quarrel in the Morning

A Quarrel in the Morning

ONE EARLY morning, just as the sun was getting up, a long, fat worm wriggled over the grass to his hole. He had been out all night long, enjoying himself, and now he was tired and wanted to rest in the little round room that was at the end of his hole.

Suddenly he heard the tippity-tip noise of a blackbird's feet on the grass. He wriggled even more quickly, for he knew that it was time for the early birds to be about! Then he heard the hippity-hop noise of a frog jumping, and he felt about for the edge of his hole.

That's a frog leaping along! thought the worm in a

fright. *Oh, dear, where has my hole gone to? I know it's somewhere around here!*

Then there came the noise of scurrying feet, and the worm listened in alarm. 'A hedgehog! A prickly hedgehog! My goodness me, what a lot of my enemies are about this morning!'

He felt a tug at his tail. That was the blackbird!

He felt a nip at his waist. That was the hedgehog!

He felt a sticky tongue at his head. That was the frog!

'Leave me alone, leave me alone!' cried the worm.

But the blackbird, the hedgehog and the frog took no notice of him at all. They were too cross with each other.

'This is my worm!' whistled the blackbird through his bright yellow beak.

'Pardon me – mine, you mean!' croaked the frog, his eyes nearly starting out of his head with rage.

'My dear friends, you are both making a big mistake,' said the hedgehog, bristling all over. 'I smelt the worm first, long before either of you did.'

'Ah, but it was me that saw him first!' cried the frog.

'I spied him from the topmost branch of that tree,' said the blackbird angrily. 'He was wriggling along fast, trying to find his hole. I flew down at once. He is my breakfast, so you must go away and leave him to me.'

'I am going to make my breakfast of him,' said the frog, and he flicked out his long, sticky tongue. It was fastened to the front of his mouth, instead of the back, so he could flick it out quite a long way. The worm was nearly lifted into the frog's wide mouth. He would have disappeared down the frog's throat if the hedgehog hadn't suddenly knocked the frog aside with his nose.

'I shall eat him,' said the hedgehog, and he ran at the worm with his sharp muzzle. But the blackbird pecked him so hard that he drew back.

'Do you want to fight me?' he asked, all his prickles standing straight up. 'I can tell you, Blackbird, it is no joke to fight a prickly hedgehog like me! No animal dares to do that!'

'Oh, fiddlesticks to you!' said the blackbird rudely. 'I'm not going to fight you. I'm going to eat my worm. If you try any tricks on me I can easily spread my wings and fly off.'

'And then I shall gobble up my worm,' said the hedgehog.

'You two fight and settle it,' said the frog hopefully. 'I'll watch and tell you who wins.'

'Yes, and eat the worm while we're fighting,' said the hedgehog scornfully. 'We are not quite as stupid as that, thank you very much.'

'Look, here's a mouse,' said the frog suddenly. 'Let's ask him to be our judge.'

So they called the tiny mouse, who came over most politely and bowed to all three.

'Listen,' said the hedgehog. 'We want you to settle something for us. We each think we ought to have that worm. But we can't decide which of us shall eat it.

We would like you to do the judging.'

'Well,' said the mouse politely, scratching his left ear as he thought hard. 'Well – it seems to me that it would be a good idea if you all ran a race for the worm. The blackbird mustn't fly, though. He must hop. The frog can hop too, and the hedgehog can run.'

'What shall be the winning post?' said the blackbird.

'The worm's hole is the winning post,' said the mouse. 'Now, all of you go to the wall right over there and wait for me to give you the signal. I shall say, "One, two, three, go!"'

So they all went over to the wall. But when they got there, the hedgehog called loudly to the mouse, 'Excuse me, Mouse! I can't see the hole! Couldn't you stick something in it, so that we can see it?'

The mouse looked all round for something, but could see nothing that would do. The worm spoke to the mouse. 'May I help you?' he said. 'I could, if you liked, stick myself in the hole, and stand up straight with half my body out of the hole, so that I looked just like a winning post.'

'That's a good idea, Worm,' said the mouse.

So the worm slid into his hole, and stood halfway out of it, very straight and stiff, for all the world like a little winning post.

'Can you see now?' shouted the mouse.

'Yes!' called back the others.

'Then, one, two, three, GO!' shouted the mouse.

The frog leapt high. The blackbird hopped for all he was worth. The hedgehog ran as if he moved by clockwork, all his four little legs working together. And they all arrived at the winning post at exactly the same moment!

'Who's won, who's won?' cried the frog.

'All of you,' said the mouse. 'You, Blackbird, can have the end of the worm; you the head, Frog; and you the middle, Hedgehog. Goodbye!'

He scurried off. The blackbird, the hedgehog and the frog turned to the wormhole. But the worm was gone. He no longer stuck out stiff and straight. He had wriggled down to his little room and was coiled up there, laughing to himself.

'Come up, worm!' shouted the frog, in a rage.

'I want the middle of you!' cried the hedgehog.

'I want my share of you too!' cried the blackbird.

'Well, I'm sorry,' called back the worm, 'but I'm afraid I want the whole of me. Now go away. I'm sleepy.'

The three looked at one another. 'Why didn't we share him between us when we had the chance?' said the frog. 'Well, well, never mind. We'll do that next time we catch him.'

But that worm is going to be very careful now – so I don't expect there will be a next time, do you?

A Muddle of Pixies

A Muddle of Pixies

ONCE THE three pixies, Peri, Patter and Pipkin, decided to go for a walk to Bumblebee Common. Peri wasn't quite ready so Patter and Pipkin said they would start off without him, and Peri would catch them up as soon as he could.

So off went Patter and Pipkin, arm-in-arm, merrily singing their favourite song. The sun was shining brightly and they were *so* happy.

Now, as they went through the village, little Edward, the fat teddy bear who lived in Bruin Cottage with his father and mother, came tearing down the street on his new scooter. When he saw the two pixies taking up nearly all the pavement he tried to stop – and he couldn't. He wobbled dreadfully, trying to stop himself from going into a pixie – but it was no use.

Thud – bang – kerplonk! The scooter ran into Pipkin and knocked him flat on his back. Patter was all right, though he got a shock. Edward the bear rolled into the gutter, but he was so fat that he wasn't hurt at all. The scooter ran on down the hill and went straight into Goody Two-Shoes' shoe shop, which gave her a dreadful fright.

Pipkin didn't get up. He just lay there, making queer sorts of grunts and groans, and Patter was quite frightened. 'You've hurt your knee,' he said to Pipkin. 'And you've bumped your head! And you've hurt your shoulder too, I think! Oh, poor Pipkin! No, don't try and get up! I'll go and get help at once. Stay here till a doctor comes.'

Patter ran off in a hurry. He soon found a doctor's house and rang the bell. The doctor was a gnome with a long beard, and big pointed feet and ears. As soon as he heard of poor Pipkin's accident, he took up his bag to go to help him.

'You had better go straight home and get a nice hot-water bottle in his bed, and make some milk hot for him,' said Dr Longbeard. 'I'll bring him along in my car.'

Patter was very grateful. He ran home at once, taking a short cut, so he didn't see Pipkin again. He knew the doctor would be where Pipkin was in a few moments.

Now Pipkin did not like lying flat in the road. It was very hard. So he sat up. He found that he wasn't so badly hurt after all! His shoulder was still sore, his head had a bump and his knee was grazed – but really, he wasn't very bad!

'I shall get up and go home,' he said. 'I can walk, if I limp a bit. Patter was silly to go rushing off to a doctor like that.'

So off went Pipkin, limping home.

Now Peri, who had been left at home clearing up,

had soon finished his bit of work and set off after the others. He had with him his collection of postcards and he was looking at them as he went. Suddenly they slipped out of his hand and down they went into the road! Peri knelt down to pick them up.

And at the very same moment Dr Longbeard, who was driving along in his car, looking out for a pixie somewhere in the street, saw Peri on his knees in the road.

'There's the poor old hurt pixie!' he said to himself. 'Hasn't even been able to stand up yet! Well, I'll soon put him right!'

He stopped the car and jumped out. He hurried to Peri, who looked up in surprise.

'Just let me bandage your head up first,' said Dr Longbeard, and he took out a big white bandage. 'Where's the bump? Dear, dear, you've such a lot of hair that I can hardly feel your head through it! Never mind – if I bandage the whole of your head that's sure to include the bump!'

'I don't want my head bandaged,' said Peri in alarm, wondering whatever the doctor was doing.

'No, no, I'm sure you don't,' said the doctor. 'Now, now, be brave, be brave! I'll rub your shoulder next. You may have sprained it.'

'I don't want my shoulder rubbed,' said Peri, getting cross. 'Ooh! You hurt! Don't rub so hard!'

'Dear, dear, does it hurt very much?' said Dr Longbeard. 'Well, you must have had a very hard fall, yes, you must. Now for the knee.'

'I don't know what you're talking about,' said Peri angrily, and he tried to jerk his leg away from Dr Longbeard. 'Don't do it – what are you tying my leg up for? Oh, you've done it so tightly that I can't walk!'

'Poor fellow, poor fellow,' said the gnome. 'Here is a crutch to lean on. You'll soon be all right now!'

Very angry indeed, poor Peri was bundled into the doctor's car and driven home. When he got there the doctor bustled out and went to the door. 'Have you got the bed ready, and the hot milk?'

he called to Patter.

'Yes, bring him in!' shouted Patter. Then up the path, hopping along with his crutch, came poor puzzled Peri, wondering if everyone was quite, quite mad.

Patter met him at the door – and he stared and he stared.

'But, Peri,' said Patter, 'I thought it was Pipkin that had had the accident, not you! Am I mad? Surely it was Pipkin!'

'Everybody's mad,' said Peri. 'I was just picking up some postcards I'd dropped when along came this doctor fellow and bandaged my head and pulled my shoulder about and tied up my knee so tightly I couldn't walk! Where's Pipkin?'

'There he is!' said Patter – and sure enough there came Pipkin limping up the street looking very dusty and sorry for himself!

'You've bandaged the wrong pixie!' said Patter to the surprised doctor. 'Oh my, oh my – he's bandaged the wrong pixie!'

Patter began to laugh – and then Peri began – and when poor Pipkin limped up to the front door he could not *imagine* what was the matter with them!

'How unkind of you to laugh at me when I'm hurt,' said poor Pipkin.

'Bandage this pixie, doctor,' said Patter. But Dr Longbeard shook his head.

'No,' he said. 'I'm not bandaging any more pixies today. Goodbye!' And off he went.

So Patter took off Peri's bandages and put them on Pipkin, who was very proud of them. And now he is sitting up in bed, hugging a hot-water bottle and drinking hot milk and feeling very happy indeed. What a muddle, wasn't it?

Lightwing the Swallow

Lightwing the Swallow

LIGHTWING CAME out of a white egg in a nest made of mud. He was very tiny indeed, and at first he could see nothing in the dark barn where his mother and father had built their nest. But very soon his eyes made out the high rafters above him, and the beam on which his nest was put.

He looked at a hole in the barn roof through which he could see the blue sky. It was summertime, so the sky was often blue. Lightwing crouched down in the nest with his brother and sister, and waited impatiently for his mother and father to come with titbits to eat.

He was a funny little thing, rather bare, with very

few feathers at first. But gradually they grew, and soon Lightwing and his brother and sister were fluffy nestlings, sitting with ever-open beaks waiting for flies that their parents caught on the wing outside the big barn.

Lightwing was a swallow. He had a marvellous steel-blue back, a white vest, and a streak of chestnut-red across his chest. His legs were small and his beak was wide in its gape. His wings were long and his tail was forked prettily. He longed for the day to come when he might fly off with his father and mother.

But when the day came he was rather afraid! His brother flew out of the nest and through the door as if he had been used to flying all his short life – but Lightwing and his sister sat on the edge of the nest, trembling. Their mother suddenly flew behind them and tipped them off the nest!

Lightwing fell – but as he fell he opened his wings, and lo and behold he could fly! His wings flashed through the barn door – he was up in the air and away, rejoicing to be in the clear, sunny blue sky.

He learnt to catch flies on the wing with his mouth wide open. He learnt to skim the water and pick up the flies hovering over the surface. He knew that when rain was coming the flies flew lower, and he followed them. When the weather was fine the flies flew high, and Lightwing soared below the clouds, following his food there. Then people said, 'The swallows fly high – it will be fine,' or, 'The swallows fly low – there will be rain.'

Lightwing grew strong and tireless as he flew throughout the warm summer days. But one night there was a chill in the air. Lightwing was surprised. He did not like it.

'Winter is coming!' sang the robin in his creamy voice.

'What is winter?' cried Lightwing, in his pretty twitter. 'Is it something to eat?'

One night a chill north-west wind began to blow.

Lightwing felt restless. He wanted to fly somewhere, but he did not know where. He wanted to go where he could no longer feel the cold wind. He flew to the barn roof to ask his friends what to do. Hundreds of swallows settled on the old red roof. They chattered and twittered restlessly. The wind blew behind them.

And then, quite suddenly, a few swallows rose up into the air and flew southwards, with the chill wind behind them. In a few moments all the waiting hundreds had risen, too, and with one accord flew to the south.

'Goodbye!' called the robin. 'Goodbye till the spring!'

Lightwing called goodbye and flew with the others. Over land and over sea sped the swallows, as fast as express trains, to a warmer, southern land, where flies were plentiful and the sun was hot.

And there Lightwing is now – but when the spring comes again he will return, and maybe build his nest in your barn or mine!

Mother Hubbard's
Honey

Mother Hubbard's Honey

MOTHER HUBBARD kept bees, and they made lovely golden honey for her. Mother Hubbard took it from the hives and put it into jars.

Then, for once, her cupboard was full when she went to it, instead of bare. Row upon row of honey jars stood there, waiting to be sold.

Now little Pixie Peep-About lived next door to Mother Hubbard, and he loved honey. But he wasn't a very good or very helpful pixie, so Mother Hubbard didn't give him any honey. She sold most of it, gave some to her friends and kept six pots for herself.

Pixie Peep-About was cross because she never gave

him any honey. 'And I live next door, too!' he said to himself. 'She might give me just a taste. She knows I love honey.'

But Peep-About never gave Mother Hubbard any of his gooseberries when they were ripe. And he didn't offer her an egg when his hens laid him plenty. So it wasn't surprising that he didn't get any honey.

One summer he watched Mother Hubbard's bees. 'How busy they are,' he said as he peeped over the wall. 'In and out, in and out of those hives all the day long. And what is more, a lot of those bees come into my garden and take the nectar from my flowers!'

It was quite true. They did. But bees go anywhere and everywhere, so of course they went into Peep-About's garden too.

Some of that honey they are storing in Mother Hubbard's hives is mine, made from nectar from my flowers, thought Peep-About. *So Mother Hubbard ought to give me plenty!*

He told Mother Hubbard this, but she laughed.

'Nectar is free in the flowers,' she said. 'Don't be silly, Peep-About.'

Now, one day Mother Hubbard went to take the honeycombs from her hives. They were beautiful combs, full of golden honey. She meant to separate the honey from the combs and store it in her jars. Peep-About knew she was going to do that. She did it every year.

Now she'll have jar upon jar of honey, and she won't give me a single one, thought the pixie. *It's too bad. I haven't tasted honey for months, and I should love some on a bit of bread and butter.*

Mother Hubbard poured the honey into her jars. She handed one to old Mr Potter, at the bottom of the garden. He was a kind old fellow and always gave Mother Hubbard tomatoes when he had some to spare. He was delighted.

'Look at that now,' said Peep-About to himself. 'Not a drop for me. Mean old thing!' My, what delicious honey it looked.

The next day Mother Hubbard dressed herself up in her best, and set out to catch the bus, with three pots of honey in her basket. Peep-About met her as she went to the bus stop.

'Where are you going?' asked Peep-About.

'To see my sister, Dame Blue-Bonnet,' said Mother Hubbard. 'I'll be gone all day, so if you see the milkman, Peep-About, tell him to leave me a pint of milk.'

Gone all day, thought Peep-About. *Well, what about me getting in at the kitchen window, going to that cupboard and helping myself to a few spoonfuls of honey!*

So, when Mother Hubbard was safely on the bus, Peep-About crept in at her kitchen window and went to the cupboard. It wasn't locked. He opened it and saw row upon row of jars of honey. Oh, what a lovely sight!

He was small and the cupboard was high. He tried to scramble up to one of the shelves and he upset a jar of honey. Down it went and poured all over him!

'Gracious!' said Peep-About in alarm. 'It's all

over me! How lovely it tastes!'

He thought he had better go back to his own home, scrape the honey off himself and eat it that way. So out of the window he went.

But the garden was full of Mother Hubbard's bees and they smelt the honey on Peep-About at once.

'Zzzzzz! Honey! ZZZZZZZ! Honey!' they buzzed to one another, and flew round Peep-About. They tried to settle on the honey that was running down his head and neck.

'Go away! Go away! Stop buzzing round me!' he cried. But no matter how he beat them away, back they came again.

Peep-About had a terrible time, for wherever he went the bees went too. They followed him into his kitchen. They stung him when he flapped them away. They followed him out into the garden again. They followed him into the street. They wouldn't leave Peep-About alone for one minute.

He couldn't sit down and have his lunch. He had to

go without his tea. He ran here and he ran there, but always the bees flew with him.

He had their honey on him, and they wanted it.

More and more bees came to join in the fun. At last Peep-About saw Mother Hubbard walking up her front path and he ran to her. She was astonished to see her bees round him in a big buzzing cloud.

'Take them away! Make them go to their hive!' wept Peep-About.

Mother Hubbard touched him and found he was sticky with honey. Then she knew what had happened.

'You went to steal some of my honey,' she said sternly. 'You're a bad pixie. You can keep the honey – and the bees too! I shan't call them off!'

So, until the bees went to bed in their hive that night, poor Peep-About had to put up with them. He ran for miles trying to get rid of them, but he couldn't. They could fly faster than he could run.

At last the bees went to bed. Peep-About stripped off his sticky suit and washed it. He got himself a meal. He cried all the time. 'I shall never like honey again,' he wept. 'Never, never, never!'

The next day Mother Hubbard was sorry that she hadn't helped poor Peep-About, even though he had been a bad little pixie. So she sent him in a tiny jar of honey all for himself.

But wasn't it a pity – he couldn't eat it! He didn't like honey any more. He couldn't bear to look at it.

'It serves me right,' he said. 'When I couldn't have it, I loved it and tried to take it. Now, here I've got a jar and I can't bear to eat it. It's a good punishment for me, it really is!'

He was right. It was!

The Meddlesome
Butterfly

The Meddlesome Butterfly

THERE WAS once a white butterfly who was very meddlesome. If there was something it could poke its feelers into, it would! The brownies and the pixies used to be very annoyed with it when it flew in at their windows to see what cakes they were baking that day or who they were having to tea!

One day the brownie Lightfoot thought he would decorate his house from top to bottom. As he lived in a tiny house under the hawthorn hedge and had only two rooms, this was not a very big job.

I'll shut my doors and windows, and do the work without telling anyone, he thought. *Then I'll give a party, and how surprised my friends will be to see my house all bright and new inside!*

So he shut the doors and windows and set to work. He was fond of bright colours, so he decided to paint his bedroom green and his kitchen orange. My word, what a busy time he had!

He didn't go out to shop. He didn't go out to buy a newspaper or hear the news. He sent his friends the earwigs, the spiders and the butterflies to get him all he wanted. But he wouldn't let the meddlesome white butterfly do anything, because Lightfoot knew perfectly well that once that butterfly got his long feelers inside the door he would smell out his secret, and would tell everyone how Lightfoot was painting his house – and then it wouldn't be a surprise any more.

This made the white butterfly very angry. And one night when Lightfoot was in bed the butterfly flew softly down to the tiny house on his powdery wings and pushed at the door. For once Lightfoot had forgotten to lock it, and it opened. The butterfly went inside.

He went round and round the kitchen looking for matches to light a candle. His wings brushed against the walls as he felt for a shelf where the brownie might keep his matches.

He knocked over a bottle of milk. He blundered into a basket of eggs and upset those. Crash! That frightened him, for he heard Lightfoot jumping out of bed. He scurried to the door, knocking over a pot of paint on the way. Meddlesome little butterfly!

Lightfoot was so angry in the morning when he found his eggs broken, his milk upset and his paint overturned. He asked everyone who it was that had done so much damage, but no one had any idea at all.

The meddlesome butterfly felt quite sure that nobody would guess it had been him in the little house. So he spread his wings boldly and flew down to the crowd of people round Lightfoot's house.

And as soon as he sat beside them everyone knew that it had been the meddlesome butterfly who had been in Lightfoot's house. How did they know?

Yes – the tips of his wings had brushed the wet paint on the wall and had coloured them orange! 'It's you who was here last night!' cried Lightfoot in a rage, and caught him and used him to fly on for the rest of the summer.

When the Sun Rises

When the Sun Rises

IT WAS night time. Everywhere was dark. The little birds were all asleep in the trees and hedges and the rabbits were down in their holes. Only the red fox was out, hunting, and the big owl hooted as it looked for mice in the fields.

'The night is very long,' said a little sparrow to his brother.

'It will soon be over now,' said his brother.

'It is very cold,' said a thrush, waking up and stretching his brown wings.

'When the sun rises it will be warm,' said the blackbird.

A small rabbit put his head out of his burrow.

'I can see a grey light in the sky!' he called to his mother.

'Come here,' said his mother. 'The red fox is about. Wait till the sun rises and then you can go out safely, for the fox will go to his hole then.'

The grey light in the sky grew brighter. Then slowly, slowly, it turned to pale gold – then to bright gold. The sun was coming!

'Chirrup-chirrup-chirrup!' twittered the sparrows, waking up one after another. 'The sun is rising!'

The blackbird opened his orange beak and sang a song to welcome the sun. 'The night was cold, so cold!' he sang. 'But now the sky is gold!'

'Come and see, come and see, come and see!' sang the freckled thrush.

'Look, look!' cried the little rabbit, running out of his hole in the grass. 'Here comes the big, round, golden sun!'

All the birds looked. Many rabbits came from their

holes and watched. Some butterflies sleeping on the flowers awoke, stretched their pretty wings and fluttered up into the air to see the golden sun come slipping up into the sky. What a big round ball it looked! How bright it was! How warm!

'The sky is red and gold!' called the starling from the tree-top. 'The little clouds are red and gold too. I wish I had feathers of red and gold! How beautiful I should be!'

The rabbits scampered out into the early sunshine. They nibbled the grass. They were delighted to welcome the sun.

A lark awoke in the field. He felt the warmth of the rising sun on his brown feathers. He lifted up the crest on his head in delight. He had his nest in the field and his wife and babies were there. He was happy.

'Here is the beautiful sun again!' he sang to his wife. 'I must fly up, up, up into the sky to get as near him as I can, and tell him all about our dear little family.' So up he flew into the sky, up and up until the rabbits could only see a little black speck. But they could hear his beautiful song. It came pouring down from the sky as the lark flew higher and higher.

'I love the sun, the sun, the sun,' he sang. 'It warms my little ones, it makes the world so bright and lovely, I love the shining sun!'

'Pink, pink!' said the pretty little chaffinch, waking up in the hedge. 'The clouds are pink, pink! The sun has risen again. It is daytime!'

The two robins flew to the hedge-top and sang their creamy song of joy. 'Here is another lovely day. The sun went away last night and left the world dark and cold. Now he is back again and everything is beautiful! We love the sun!'

Acknowledgements

All efforts have been made to seek necessary permissions.

The stories in this publication first appeared in the following publications:

'Too Good to Be True!' first appeared in *Enid Blyton's Sunny Stories*, No. 422, 1948.

'Brer Rabbit's Strange Flower' first appeared in *The Teachers World*, No. 1694/1695, 1935.

'The Knotty Handkerchief' first appeared in *Sunny Stories for Little Folks*, No. 178, 1933.

'Caterpillar Party' first appeared in *Enid Blyton's Sunny Stories*, No. 408, 1947.

'Mr Twiddle Fetches Polly' first appeared in *Enid Blyton's Magazine*, No. 15, Vol. 3, 1955.

'The Pixie in the Pond' first appeared in *Enid Blyton's Sunny Stories*, No. 40, 1937.

'Wagger Goes to the Show' first appeared in *Enid Blyton's Sunny Stories*, No. 407, 1947.

'Plum Jam' first appeared in *Enid Blyton's Sunny Stories*, No. 413, 1947.

'The Train That Lost Its Way' was first published by Brockhampton Press in 1946.

'The Bee Is A Busy Postman' first appeared in *Sunday Mail*, No. 1924, 1945.

'Blackberry Tart' first appeared in *Enid Blyton's Sunny Stories*, No. 145, 1939.

'Gillian and Bobs Have an Adventure' first appeared in *Tales of Old Thatch*, first published in 1938 by W. & A. K. Johnston.

'Peter's New Shoes' is an untraced story.

'The Little Horse-Tricycle' first appeared in *Sunny Stories for Little Folks*, No. 234, 1936.

'Paying It Back' first appeared in *Enid Blyton's Sunny Stories*, No. 215, 1941.

'The Runaway Shoes' first appeared in *Enid Blyton's Sunny Stories*, No. 139, 1939.

'The Poppy Pixie' first appeared in *Enid Blyton's Sunny Stories*, No. 85, 1938.

'Mr Twiddle Cuts the Grass' first appeared as 'Twiddle Cuts the Grass' in *Enid Blyton's Sunny Stories*, No. 413, 1947.

'The Two Poor Children' first appeared in *Enid Blyton's Sunny Stories*, No. 129, 1939.

'Pretty-Star the Pony' first appeared in *Sunny Stories for Little Folks*, No. 81, 1929.

'The Tin Whistle' first appeared in *Enid Blyton's Sunny Stories*, No. 175, 1940.

'The Dog Who Would Go Digging' first appeared in *Sunny Stories for Little Folks*, No. 182, 1934.

'Rufus Pays Back' first appeared in *Enid Blyton's Sunny Stories*, No. 332, 1944.

'Impy Plays a Trick' first appeared in *Enid Blyton's Sunny Stories*, No. 86, 1938.

'A Quarrel in the Morning' first appeared in *Enid Blyton's Sunny Stories*, No. 282, 1942.

'A Muddle of Pixies' first appeared in *Three Bold Pixies*, first published by Award in 1994.

'Lightwing the Swallow' first appeared in *The Teachers World*, No. 1844, 1938.

'Mother Hubbard's Honey' first appeared in *Enid Blyton's Sunny Stories*, No. 360, 1945.

'The Meddlesome Butterfly' first appeared in *The Teachers World*, No. 1827, 1938.

'When the Sun Rises' first appeared in *Two Years in the Infant School: Topics 22–42*, first published by George Newnes in 1938.